DISNEY LEARNING

Disney · PIXAR

Reading, Writing, and Math

GRADE 2

NELSON

This workbook belongs to:

_____

Disney LEARNING

Published by Nelson Education Ltd.

ISBN-13: 978-0-17-682802-8
ISBN-10: 0-17-682802-8

Printed and bound in Canada
1 2 3 4   20 19 18 17

For more information contact Nelson Education Ltd., 1120 Birchmount Road, Toronto, Ontario M1K 5G4. Or you can visit our website at nelson.com.

Contents

Alphabet Blast Attack

The alphabet has been blasted!

What letters are missing?

Fill in the missing capital letters below.

A B C ___ E F G

H ___ J K L ___ N

O P Q ___ S T U

V ___ X Y Z

What letters are missing?

Fill in the missing lowercase letters below.

a b c d ____ f

g ____ i j k ____ m

n o ____ q r s

t ____ v w x ____ z

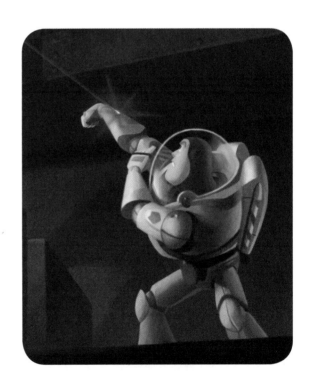

Learn Together Play a game with your child: say the alphabet, pausing randomly so your child can name a word beginning with the last letter you listed.

3

Clean Up the Letters

Can Dory find her parents?

Did you notice that the words in the above sentence are in alphabetical order?

Alphabetical **order** is when the letters of the alphabet are in the correct sequence.

A B C D E F G H I J K L M N O
P Q R S T U V W X Y Z

Put these words in alphabetical order to make another sentence.

her parents finds Dory

_____

These letters are in a mess!

Put each group of letters in alphabetical order.

The first one has been done for you.

B D A

A B D

Z R M

_____

c g e n

_____

x u p k

_____

T w i P

_____

m Y I D

_____

k q p A

_____

Z s A e

_____

Alphabet Rescue!

An incredible family saves the world!

Did you notice that the words in the above sentence are in alphabetical order?

Put these words in alphabetical order.

fast   strong   incredible

_____

robot   hero   save

_____

team   super   mask

_____

trick   defeat   mission

_____

island   secret   beat

_____

home   force   plane

_____

Learn Together Help your child read the words and sort them into alphabetical order. Use some of these words to tell a story about the Incredibles and a mission they experience.

7

Lasso Those Letters!

W   L

R   B   J   H   S

A

O

Herd these names into alphabetical order.

Roundup   Bullseye   Jessie

_____

Woody   Andy   Buzz

_____

Sarge   Rex   Hamm

_____

Put these words in alphabetical order
to create a sentence.

Woody   Buzz   helps

_____.

umbrella   the   Jessie   lassos

_____.

trots   Bullseye   quickly

_____.

puns   likes   Hamm

_____.

Learn Together
Challenge your child to create a sentence with all the words in alphabetical order. How many words can they use and still have all of them in alphabetical order? (A two-word sentence is easier than three, three easier than four, and so on.).

Missing Letters

Can you figure out which letter is missing?

_____ainbow   _____elp

_____obster   _____other

l

h   m   r

Read each word out loud.

Listen to the sound of the first letter.

Add the missing letters.

h   l   r   m

Dory ___oses ___er dad and ___om.

___ow will she find the ___ight way to go?

___osing them ___akes ___er sad.

Read each sentence out loud.

Listen to the letter sounds.

Write your own sentence about Dory.

_____

_____

Who Will Win the Next Race?

Can you figure out which letter is missing?

n

s

t

w

_____eason   _____ater

_____axi   _____ighttime

Read each word out loud.

Listen to the sound of the first letter.

Draw something that begins with **n**, **s**, **t**, or **w**.

Add the missing letters.

Natalie Certain ____ants ____o predict
the ____ext ____inner.

Lightning McQueen ____ants ____o race.

"____ime for ____he race!" ____ays
Natalie Certain.

n

s

t

w

Read each sentence out loud.

Listen to the letter sounds.

Learn Together

Help your child sound out the words and use
context to complete the sentences. Emphasize
the consonant sounds as you say each word.

Decode the Secret Messages!

Dash has received a secret message.

Decode the message for him.

___ecode this message: k

___arty tonight!   p

___o to the ___arden ___ate.   d

Bring a ___ite and a ___ey.   g

Read the message out loud.

Listen to the letter sounds.

Add the missing letters.

g   p   d   k

___ash is faster than

a ___angaroo.

___o, ___ash, ___o!!

He leaves the ___ack ___anting behind!

Those ___ids can't ___eep up.

___eople in the crowd
cheer ___ash on.

Read each sentence out loud.

Listen to the letter sounds.

Learn Together

Your child may notice that **c** and **k** can make the same sound. Talk about other letters that make the same sound (**c** and **s**).

The End of It All

It's a dark and stormy night, Woody!

Add the missing letter to the end of each word.

frigh_____   fro_____   d   m

loo_____   ma_____   t   k

Read each word out loud.

Listen to the sound of the last letter.

Add the missing letter to
the end of each word.

d   ^t   m   k

Woody will nee__ war__ clothes
on a col__, dar__ nigh__.

Does he wan__ to hide under the be__
or rea__ a boo__?

Is Woody afrai__ of the tric__ or treaters?

Le__ hi__ know everything will be O__.

Read each sentence out loud.

Listen to the letter sounds.

Learn Together   Help your child try each of the four letters until they find the right one. Note that more than one letter will work on page 16 (look, loom, loot; mat, mad). For each sentence, they can use context to figure out the right letter.

Stop Those Evil Villains!

The Incredibles have a job
to do—stopping the evil villains!

You have a job, too!
Add the missing letter to the end of each word.

p   x   f   l

bo_____   co_____

coo_____   roo_____

Read each word out loud.

Listen to the sound of the last letter.

Use one of the words to write a sentence about
The Incredibles.

_____

Add the missing letter to the end of each word.

Where two letters are missing in a word, it is the same two letters.

Can The Incredibles sto___ a___ ___ o___ the evi___ villains?

Wi___ ___ they pu___ ___ o___ ___ the rescue i___ they have the right ma___?

They wi___ ___ try to foo___ Syndrome and fi___ their jet.

p

l

f

x

Read each sentence out loud.

Listen to the letter sounds.

Learn Together Discuss how some of the words (off, pull, will) have double consonants at the end. With your child, list rhyming words for some of the words above (cop, stop, hop; cool, pool, fool). Emphasize the ending sound as you read the list over.

Happy Endings

The hermit crabs are mad. Dory needs to flee.

Add the missing letter to the end of each word.

b   s   n   g

crab___   fro___

cra___   dow___

Read each word out loud.

Listen to the sound of the last letter.

Add the missing letters.

Whe___ Dory searche___ for her family,   **b**

every cra___ trie___ to stop her.   **s**

Ca___ she find them soo___?   **n**

Dory ha___ a bi___ problem she need___   **g**
to solve!

Read each sentence out loud.

Listen to the letter sounds.

Learn Together

List other **plural words**, listening to the final letter **s** sound (homes, rocks, helmets).

Cap or Cape?

The letter **a** can make a short vowel sound, as in **cap**.

It can also make a long vowel sound, as in **cape**. Long vowels sound like their letter names.

Say each word out loud.
Listen for the vowel sound.

(Circle) the words with a short vowel **a** sound.

ape   bad   rake   mask   grab

grape   Dash   race

Underline the words with a long vowel **a** sound.

apple   raid   mad   brake   cat

shake   tame   brain

The letter **e** can make a short vowel sound, as in **men**. It can also make a long vowel sound, as in **mean**.

(Circle) the words with a short vowel **e** sound.

bet　　bee　　jet　　send　　get

bead　　feed　　red

Underline the words with a long vowel **e** sound.

fed　　beat　　met　　meal　　meet

set　　we　　test

Learn Together　With your child, identify the vowel pattern or rule in some of the words above (When two vowels appear together in a word, the first vowel is usually long and the second is silent, as in *maid* and *beat*.).

The Fin Is Fine

The letter i can make a
short vowel sound, as in **fin**.

It can also make a long vowel sound, as in **fine**.

Say each word out loud.
Listen for the vowel sound.

(Circle) the words with a short vowel i sound.

bite   bit   fine   rib

side   if   big

Underline the words with a long vowel i sound.

I   sit   write   kite   igloo

ice   it   line

The letter **o** can make a short vowel sound, as in **not**.

It can also make a long vowel sound, as in **note**.

(Circle) the words with a short vowel **o** sound.

boat   rock   rope   rob   robe

odd   top   mole

Underline the words with a long vowel **o** sound.

open   road   lock   ocean   old

soak   code   pod

Learn Together

With your child, look for patterns in these words (A silent **e** at the end of a word—*robe*—makes the vowel in the middle long. Most three-letter words with a consonant, vowel, consonant have a short vowel sound—*rob*.).

Up, Up, and Away!

The letter **u** can make a short vowel sound, as in **us**.

It can also make a long vowel sound, as in **use**.

Say each word out loud.

Listen for the vowel sound.

Circle the words with a short vowel **u** sound.

cut   cute   but   buggy   cub

truck   sun   music

Underline the words with a long vowel **u** sound.

uniform   unicorn   dull   huge

unit   bug   fuse

The letter **y** can sometimes act as a vowel.

What letter sound does the **y** make in **baby**? _____

What letter sound does the **y** make in **cry**? _____

Say each of these words out loud.

Write the vowel sound you hear.

The first one has been done for you.

cry __**i**__   sky _____   try _____

lazy _____   oily _____   funny _____

The letter **y** can sometimes work with
a vowel to make a long vowel sound.

Say these words out loud: **say   they   tray   way**

Learn Together

Discuss the vowel sounds. In the **ay** words, the **y** acts
to make the **a** long. In *they*, the **y** does not make a long
e sound. As your child's reading skills develop, they will
notice many other exceptions to general rules.

Sarge Battles R

Sometimes, other letters can
make vowels sound different.

For example, in the word **Sarge**,
a sounds different when followed by **r**.

The **a** in Sarge does not sound
long or short.

The **r** changes the sound of the vowel.

Add the missing vowels.

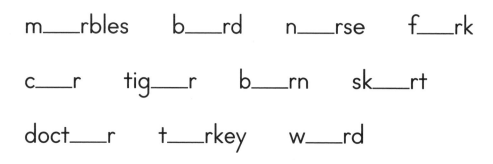

m___rbles   b___rd   n___rse   f___rk

c___r   tig___r   b___rn   sk___rt

doct___r   t___rkey   w___rd

Say each word out loud.
Listen to the vowel sound.

The letter **w** can also change
the sound of a vowel.

Read these sentences out loud.

We **saw** you through the **window**.

The **jaw yawns**.

Will you **plow** with the **cow**?

Take a **bow**, **now**.

Listen to the vowel sound in the **purple** words.

Did you notice that you don't pronounce
the **w** on its own?

The vowel plus **w** makes one sound.

Learn Together

Help your child figure out the missing letters. In some cases, more than one vowel will work (burn, barn; ward, word). As you read together, look for words that follow similar patterns.

Part of the Team

Sometimes, vowels work together to change a short vowel sound into a long vowel sound.

For example, in the word **team**, the **a** helps make the **e** long.

Say each word out loud. Listen to the vowel sound.

Underline the two words in each row that make the same vowel sound.

sleep   mean   bait

coat   green   deal

soap   feel   boat

The letter **e** at the end of a word can make the vowel in the middle long.

Sam becomes **same** when you add a silent **e**.

The short vowel **a** sound in **Sam** becomes a long vowel sound.

Add an **e** to the end of the **purple** words below.

Help us **us**____ the remote.

Plan to make a **plan**____.

The cop can **cop**____.

Take a bit of a **bit**____.

Say these sentences out loud.

Listen to the vowel sounds.

Learn Together

Share the following mnemonic with your child: When two vowels go walking, the first one does the talking. Note that there are exceptions to this rule (eight, bread). Help your child make other words using a silent **e**.

Freezing Words

Sometimes when two consonants work together in a word you hear both letter sounds.

For example, the **F** and **r** in **Frozone**.

Choose one pair of consonants to make a word.

br tr sl _____ick	cl fr bl _____og
fr br sn _____eeze	fl bl cl _____ock
pl st gr _____ain	dr cr st _____eam

Jack-Jack is using a spoon. What two consonants work together in **spoon**? _____

Choose one pair of consonants to make a word.

fr   tr   cl   bl   sp   sl

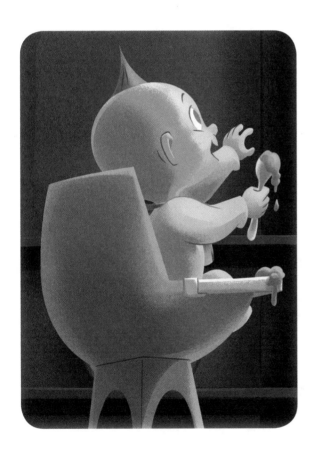

_____ap

_____og

_____eeze

_____ill

_____ot

_____ing

Learn Together Your child can make a variety of words with each consonant pair and **word ending**. See **consonant blends** in the glossary for more on how consonants work together at the beginning and end of words.

33

Sticking Together to the End

Two or more consonants can also work together at the end of a word.

Hank is Dory's **friend**.

Listen to the sounds the letters **nd** make.

Choose one pair of consonants to make a word.

lp nt lt he_____	nt nd mp ba_____	st lp rd bi_____
st pt ct te_____	pt nt mp la_____	lf nt rd elepha_____

Choose one pair of consonants to make a word.

rd   st   nt   nd   mp

Becky is a bi_____ called a loon.

Dory mu_____ ju_____ into a drain to escape.

Dory looks differe_____ from the other fish

in the ocean.

Where will Dory's story e_____?

Read the sentences out loud.

Sticking with Words

This is Nick Stickers. He likes bumper stickers.

Sometimes **when** two consonants work together in a word you hear only one sound.

For example, the **t** and **h** in **This** and the **w** and **h** in **when**.

Choose one pair of consonants to make a word.

sh th ch _____en	sh ch th _____eet	wh wr th _____ale
ch th wr _____eat	th wh ch _____orn	wh sh th _____ut
sh ch wr _____ite	wr sh ch _____eese	sh wh th _____ark

Read these bumper stickers out loud.

<u>Underline</u> the consonants that work together
to make one sound.

CHOOSE THE
CHASE!

Through Thick or Thin,
We Play to Win!

shape up
or
ship out

I stayed in sleepy
Radiator Springs.

**Where Wishes
Come True!**

Big Dreams
in the Trunk

**Learn
Together** Your child can make a variety of words with **digraphs** such as these. List other words in the **wr** or **wh** word family (write, written, wrote; whale, what, which).

Shhhh!

Buzz has hit the mute button!

Some words have letters that you don't pronounce.

These letters are called **silent letters**.

The letters **b**, **g**, **h**, **k**, and **w** are sometimes silent.

Underline the silent letters in **Buzz Lightyear's** name.

Say each of these words out loud.

Underline the silent letters.

thumb   sign   knock   wrist   light

comb   write   ghost   knife   right

Say each of these words out loud.

<u>Underline</u> the silent letters.

honest   wrist   knight   wrap   gnome

knit   lamb   character   chaos   knee

Learn Together

Create word family lists for the **silent letters**. For example, record all the words your child knows that include the letters **gh** or **kn**.

Inside Outside Words

You never know what's hiding inside!

A **compound word** is made using two smaller words.

Draw a / between the two smaller words in the word **inside**.

Draw a / between the two smaller words inside each word below.

The first one has been done for you.

can/not   anybody   campfire   today

anyone   everything   basketball   without

cupcake   sunshine   rainfall   forever

Match a word on the left to a word on
the right to make a compound word.

finger	**bird**
home	**print**
humming	**pack**
fire	**work**
back	**place**

(Circle) the compound words below.

broomstick   greener   airport   jackpot

forever   jacket   sadness   daycare

Don't Forget, We're Superheroes

A **contraction** is a word that is made by joining two words.

An **apostrophe** takes the place of any missing letters.

Match each contraction below with the two words that have been joined.

don't	I am
we're	you are
you're	he is
I'm	do not
he's	we are

Fill in the missing contraction to complete each sentence.

___ ___ ___ ' ___ ___ about to read an amazing story.

The Incredibles ___ ___ ___ ___ ___ ' ___ had any luck lately.

They ___ ___ ___ ' ___ fly their jet.

___ ___ ' ___ broken.

And that evil villain, Syndrome, is after them. ___ ___ ' ___ out to get them.

Use one of the contractions to write a sentence about superheroes.

He's

can't

haven't

It's

You're

_____

Learn Together With your child, create flash cards with a **contraction** on one side and the two words that form that contraction on the other. Use the cards to play matching games.

Not Again but Before

Prefixes are added to the start of a root word. Together, they make a new word with a different meaning.

pre + made = premade   pre + view = preview

un + happy = unhappy   un + done = undone

re + write = rewrite   re + play = replay

Think about the words above. Match up each prefix below with its meaning.

pre   **not**

un   **again**

re   **before**

Fill in the missing prefix to complete each sentence below.

You may use each prefix more than once.

Dory is ___ ___happy when she can't find her parents.

She ___ ___visits every place they have been together.

un

Dory is having trouble finding her parents, ___ ___fortunately.

re

Will her parents ever ___ ___appear?

Add a prefix to a word to make a new word.

_____ + _____ = _____

Learn Together

Help your child choose a **prefix** to complete each sentence.

45

More and Most

Suffixes are added to the end of a word
to make a new word.

For example, Lightning McQueen is **big**,
but Taco is **bigger**. Miss Fritter is the **biggest**.

Add the root word to its suffix.

Print the new word.

kind + er = _____

kind + est = _____

kind + ness = _____

long + er = _____

long + est = _____

Try adding **-er**, **-est**, and **-ness** to each of the following words.

sweet _____ _____ _____

soft _____ _____ _____

hard _____ _____ _____

Think about what each word means.

Label each wheel using **small, smaller, smallest**.

_____ _____ _____

Learn Together — With your child, read the words on the page. Help them work out the meaning of each word with its **suffix**. Encourage them to use the words in sentences.

Let's Go See the Sea

Where will Woody **wear** his boots?

Homophones are words that sound the same, but are spelled differently and mean different things.

For example, **where** and **wear**.

Read the homophones below out loud.

Listen to how the words sound.

Think about what each word means.

eight / ate   there / their

see / sea   two / too / to

What other homophones do you know?

_____

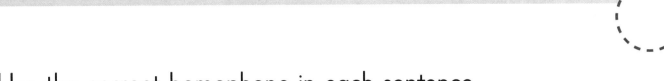

Use the correct homophone in each sentence.

We ___ ___ ___ our lunch together.   **ate   eight**

I wonder ___ ___ ___ ___ ___
Woody has gone.   **wear   where**

Bo Peep sees them going
over ___ ___ ___ ___ ___.   **there   their**

What do you want ___ ___ do
today?   **too   two   to**

Why do you ___ ___ ___ ___
that cowboy hat, Woody?   **where   wear**

Learn Together With your child, make **homophone** flash cards. How many can you make? Use these flash cards to create sentences.

Person, Place, and Thing

A **noun** is a word for a person, a place, or a thing.

Read the nouns out loud.

person: mother   teacher   doctor   Jack-Jack

place: country   city   school   house

thing: pencil   cat   fork   ball

In the sentences below, the nouns have been underlined:

The <u>heroes</u> arrive <u>home</u> to find <u>Syndrome</u> waiting.

The <u>villain</u> snatches up <u>Jack-Jack</u>, and races off to his <u>jet</u>.

The <u>baby</u> turns into a <u>mini-monster</u> in his <u>arms</u>.

Underline the nouns in each sentence.

Mr. Incredible has strong arms that can lift boulders.

Can Dash run faster than a rocket heading to the moon?

Elastigirl can stretch her whole body around a car.

The villain reveals his evil plan as he rises into the sky.

Learn Together

With your child, list five people, five places, and five things. Help your child make silly sentences using the items on the list (*Dad*, *kitchen*, and *spoon* can become "Dad is dancing with a spoon in the kitchen.").

Action!

A **verb** is an action word.

A verb often follows a noun.

The verb is the "doing" word.

<u>Underline</u> the verbs below.

swim   purple   play   talk   look   Dory

food   sing   ocean   laugh   eat   learn

Pick an action word.

Draw a picture of Dory doing that action.

When you add a verb to a sentence, how the verb is spelled depends on the noun it appears with. **We swim** fast, but **she swims** faster.

<u>Underline</u> the verbs below. Think about how the verb is spelled.

Dory sees lots of other fish in the ocean. I see Dory.

Dory looks for her parents. Her parents look for her, too.

Dory has a yellow tail. I have no tail.

Dory plays with her friends in the ocean. I play with my friends at school.

Learn Together Your child is probably already following the rules for **verbs** and nouns as they speak. Practise writing sentences together using a noun and verb that agree.

Action Now and Then!

When you add a verb to a sentence, how the verb is spelled depends on **when** the action takes place.

Andy **played** yesterday.   Andy **plays** again today.

      past   present

The word **played** is the past tense of **play**.

Underline the verbs below that are in the past tense.

looked   walked   see

treated   dream   wished

Underline the verbs in the sentences below.

Think about how the verbs are spelled.

> Yesterday: The children dressed. They ate breakfast. They got on the bus. They went to school.
>
> Today: The children dress. They eat breakfast. They get on the bus. They go to school.

Write another sentence for yesterday.

_____

Write another sentence for today.

_____

Describe It!

An **adjective** is a word that describes a noun.

Riley is **happy**. The word **happy** describes **Riley**.

Add one of these adjectives to a sentence below.

big   little   blue

Riley is a __ __ __ __ __ __ girl.

Riley's eyes are __ __ __ __.

Riley has a __ __ __ problem.

Write a sentence to describe yourself.
Use an adjective.

_____

An **adverb** is a word that describes a verb.

It tells when, where, how, or what.

These are adverbs:

now, loudly, under, inside, carefully

Riley jumps around **happily**.

The word **happily** describes **how** Riley is jumping.

Add each of these adverbs to a sentence below.

softly   slowly   later   outside

Riley goes __ __ __ __ __ __ __ to play.

Riley walks __ __ __ __ __ __.

She whispers __ __ __ __ __.

Riley will be happy again __ __ __ __ __.

Learn Together Ask your child to describe household items using adjectives. Encourage them to consider colour, shapes, smells, and textures. Give your child prompts to complete with adverbs ("The turtle moved _____." "The siren blared _____.").

Evil Robot Attacks City!

Clues in the text and picture can help you make predictions.

Look at the picture. Predict what the story on page 59

is about. _____

_____.

An evil robot is attacking the city.

The Incredibles must stop it.

Mr. Incredible knows the robot is controlled
by the remote.

Frozone uses ice walls to slow down the robot.

Elastigirl aims the remote at the robot.

I'm sure that _____

will win the battle because _____

_____

_____.

That Reminds Me...

Reading stories can remind us of our own lives.

Dory forgets where her parents are.

She wants to be with them again.

Hank wants to help. He rescues Dory from the tank.

Hank helps Dory find a map.

A purple shell on the map is a clue.

Dory knows where to look next.

<u>Underline</u> the words in the story that remind you of something.

Explain any connections you made.

_____

_____ .

Learn Together Help your child read this story. Encourage them to find different ways that a story connects to their own life. Model **making connections** ("This story reminds me of a time when I was lost …"). Ask them questions ("Do you remember when you …?").

What, Where, and Who

Story elements include the plot, setting, and characters.

The **plot** is what happens—the problem or events in the story.

The **setting** is where the story happens.

The **characters** are who the story is about.

One day, a man steals Woody and takes him to his apartment.

Woody tries to escape. That's when he meets Jessie and Bullseye.

Jessie tells Woody that he is the star of a show called "Woody's Roundup."

Woody needs to decide: stay with his new friends or return to Andy and his old friends.

Circle the characters in this story.

Underline the setting.

Number the events in the story.

Learn Together

Help your child read this story and identify its elements. With your child, create another story. On a piece of paper, draw three boxes. In each box, your child can record ideas for the **story elements**: characters, setting, and plot.

What's the Big Idea?

The main idea tells what the story is about.

It can answer "who" and "what."

One day, Dory is carried away from her parents by an undertow.

Dory loses her parents for a long time.

Dory has trouble remembering things.

Dory forgets where to find her parents.

She meets her friends Nemo and Marlin.

For a while she lives with them in a coral reef.

Finally, she remembers her parents.

What is the main idea in this story?

_____

_____ .

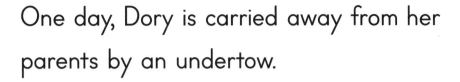

Learn Together Help your child read this story and identify the main idea. Start by discussing what the title reveals about the main idea.

Picture It!

As you read, use the words in the text to make **pictures** in your mind.

Woody and Buzz race down the street on the remote-control car.

Woody is crouched in front, leaning over the car's bumper. His face is full of fear.

A rocket is strapped to Buzz's back. Buzz sits behind Woody, holding the remote control. Buzz has a look of concentration on his face as he works the remote.

Underline the words that help you form a picture of the scene in your mind.

Describe what you see. _____

_____

_____.

Learn Together Cover up the image on page 66 as you read the description on this page so that your child has the opportunity to visualize the scene.

Look for the Clues

When you read, you put together the clues the author gives you. You "read between the lines" or **make inferences** to understand the text.

Bob, Helen, Violet, Dash, and Jack-Jack Parr live in Metroville. They all have superpowers.

Unfortunately, they are not allowed to use them in public. The Parr family pretends they are like other people. Bob is bored. Dash pretends to be a slower runner.

The whole family is worried they will never again have the chance to be superheroes. Until one day, a villain is spotted over Metroville.

How do you think the Parrs feel about not using their superpowers?

_____

_____ .

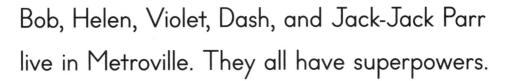

Learn Together

Read the story to your child and model **making inferences** ("I think the Parrs want to be able to use their superpowers because the text says they are worried they won't get to again.").

I Think...Because...

When you **draw conclusions**, you are forming an opinion or making a decision about what you have just read. Good conclusions are based on facts in the text.

Riley and her family move from Minnesota to San Francisco. Riley is so sad she runs away.

Joy wants Riley to be happy. She does not want Sadness to take control because Riley will be sad.

Finally, Joy learns that she and Sadness must work together to help Riley. Joy decides that Riley needs to feel sad sometimes in order to feel happy.

Do you agree with Joy's decision? Why?

_____

_____

Learn Together

Talk about this story and the questions. Help your child practise **drawing conclusions** by talking about the characters and events in other stories ("Why did the character do that? Do you think they were right? What would you have done?").

Fact or Opinion?

When you read nonfiction, **most** of the text will be **facts**.

Facts are what really happened or information that is true.

Sometimes, authors include **opinions**.

Opinions are what someone believes or thinks.

Opinions can also express a feeling.

This is a fact: Most cars have four wheels.

This is an opinion: I think all cars should be yellow.

Write **F** beside each fact and **O** beside each opinion.

_____ I think trucks are better than cars.

_____ Trucks are bigger than cars.

_____ Trucks can hold more stuff than cars.

_____ The nicest looking trucks are blue ones with big tires.

_____ Trucks are more fun to ride in than cars.

_____ Most trucks have windows.

Learn Together

Read this text to your child. With your child, write a few sentences about a topic they like (hockey, animals, music). Underline the **facts**. Write **O** beside any **opinions**. Encourage your child to support their opinions.

Tell Us About It

A **title** can tell you about the characters, the setting, and the plot of a story.

A title can give you hints about whether the story will be happy, sad, funny, or filled with action.

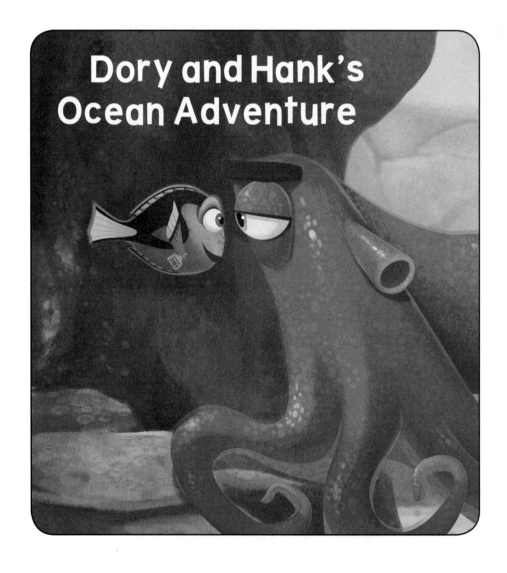

Think about a story you want to write.

Draw a picture for the story.

Write a title for it.

Learn Together Discuss your child's story ideas and the title they chose. As you read stories or watch movies, discuss their titles. Point out that the first letter of each word in a title is usually a capital.

Extra Information

Labels give you extra information.

They help you understand pictures better.

Fill in the missing labels.

blue hair

Captions are sentences that tell you what is happening in a picture.

They can give you more information about the picture.

Write a caption for each picture.

_____

_____

_____

_____

Sort It

Charts help you organize information.

Once the information is organized, it can be easier to read and understand.

Lightning McQueen has won eight practice races.

Cruz Ramirez has won three practice races.

Cal Weathers has won seven practice races.

Brick Yardley has won two practice races.

Create a chart with the information on page 78.

The first column has been filled for you.

Number of Practice Races Won

Lightning McQueen	Cruz Ramirez	Cal Weathers	Brick Yardley
8			

Who has won the most practice races?

_____

Who has won the fewest practice races?

_____

How many more practice races has Lightning McQueen

won than Cal Weathers ? _____

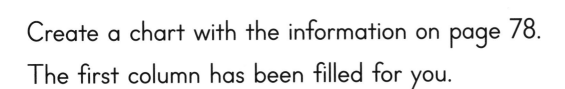

Learn Together Help your child create a **chart** about a topic that interests them. Research the information together.

Writing a Story

There are many kinds of **stories**.

There are funny stories and scary stories.

All stories have characters, a setting, and a plot.

What story does this picture tell?

Think about a story you want to tell.

Write your story.

_____

_____

_____

_____

_____

_____

_____

Learn Together

Your child might want to draw illustrations for their story before they write. Beforehand, discuss their favourite kinds of stories (scary, funny, adventure, animal, etc.). Why do they like these stories? Who are the characters? What happens?

So True!

Facts are things that are true.

You can prove facts.

For example, Woody wears brown cowboy boots.

Woody is a sheriff who lives in Andy's room.

Woody wears blue jeans, cowboy boots, and a yellow shirt.

He runs fast and rides a horse named Bullseye.

One day, Andy gets a toy called Buzz Lightyear.

Woody is jealous of the brave space ranger.

Write three facts about Woody, Bullseye, or Jessie.

1. _____

_____

_____

2. _____

_____

_____

3. _____

_____

_____

Learn Together Your child can use the picture to help them write facts. Or help your child research a character. List point-form facts that your child can use to help them write complete sentences.

Writing Sentences

Sentences end in different types of **punctuation**.

Mr. Incredible is bored by his job.

How will Mr. Incredible defeat Syndrome?

A sentence that ends with a period is telling you something.

A sentence that ends with a question mark is asking a question.

Write a sentence about The Incredibles that ends with a

period or question mark. _____

_____

The Incredibles are trapped!

Save the family, Violet!

A sentence that ends with an exclamation mark can show excitement or surprise.

An exclamation mark at the end of a sentence can also be a command.

Write a sentence about The Incredibles that ends with

an exclamation mark. _____

_____

Learn Together With your child, take turns writing sentences about yourselves that end with different punctuation marks. Remind them to use a capital letter at the beginning of each sentence.

A Small Pause

Commas are used to show pauses in sentences.

This is a comma: ,

After the race, Cruz Ramirez celebrates.

Lightning McQueen needs to be a better racer, so Cruz Ramirez becomes his trainer.

Commas can also show a list of items.

Lightning McQueen is fast, sleek, and confident.

Add the missing commas to the sentences below.

I like to eat cereal apples and toast.

_____

After eating I brush my teeth.

_____

If you ride a bike you should wear a helmet.

_____

My favourite colours are orange red and purple.

_____

Learn Together

Help your child write sentences, with commas, about their favourite character. With your child, review sentences they have written previously, looking for opportunities to include commas or other punctuation they are learning about.

Belonging and More

An **apostrophe** can be used to show
that something belongs to someone.
This is an apostrophe: '

Nemo is Marlin's son.

Dory's friends are Marlin,
Nemo, Hank, Destiny, and
Bailey.

Add an apostrophe to each sentence.

Dory s parents set out shell trails.

Hank s arms are really long.

A **contraction** is two words put together.

The missing letters are replaced by an apostrophe.

For example, **is not** becomes **isn't**.

Make contractions with the words below, adding an apostrophe.

I have ____________________ we will ____________________

we are ____________________ they have ____________________

let us ____________________ you are ____________________

he is ____________________ she is ____________________

should not ____________________ would not ____________________

Learn Together

Help your child list more contractions. Look for contractions in a story. Have your child point them out and say the two words that make the contraction.

Say It

Quotation marks show that someone is speaking. These are quotation marks: " "

These marks are often used with the words **said** or **asked**.

"Hello, Mr. Incredible," says a woman on the screen.

"Why can't we come, Mom?" Violet asks.

Look at the picture on the right. Write what Mom's reply might be. Use quotation marks.

_____

_____

Write a story about a time you played with a friend.

What did you say to each other?

Use quotation marks.

_____

_____

_____

_____

_____

_____

Learn Together Look at family photos with your child. Imagine the people in the photos are having conversations. Write down what they're saying using quotation marks.

Speed Counts

How fast can Lightning McQueen go?

Count **forward** using these number lines.

Print the missing numbers.

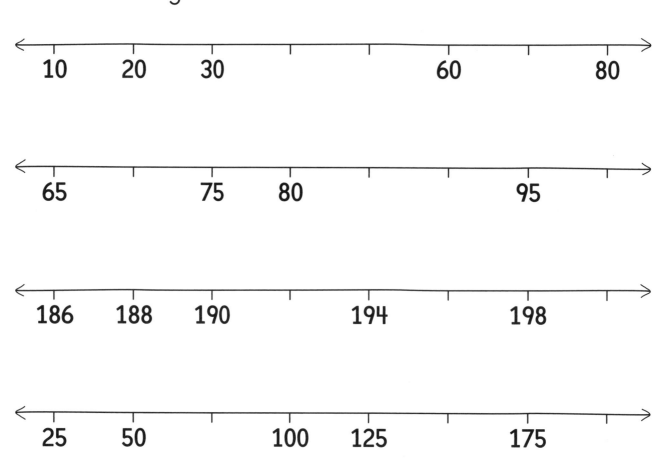

10   20   30   60   80

65   75   80   95

186 188 190   194   198

25   50   100 125   175

Print the missing numbers on the 100-chart.

100	101	102		104	105	106		108	109
110	111	112		114	115	116	117	118	119
120		122	123	124	125	126	127	128	129
	131	132	133	134	135	136	137	138	139
140	141	142	143	144	145	146	147	148	149
150	151	152	153		155	156	157	158	159
160	161	162	163	164	165	166		168	169
170	171	172	173	174	175	176	177	178	
180	181	182	183	184	185		187	188	189
190	191	192	193	194	195	196	197	198	

Learn Together

Find opportunities to practise **skip counting** to 200, either by twos, fives, or tens. You might play hide-and-seek together, bounce a ball, or jump rope.

Countdown!

How many days will it take for Dory to find her parents?

Count **backward** using these number lines.

Print the missing numbers.

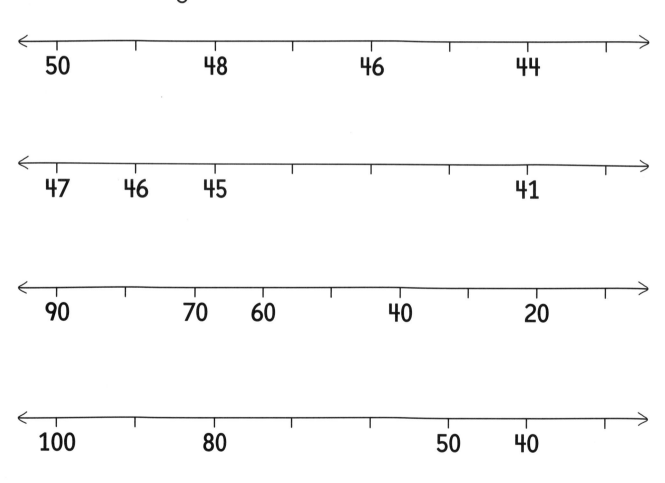

50   48   46   44

47   46   45   41

90   70   60   40   20

100   80   50   40

Print the missing numbers on the 100-chart.

100		98	97	96	95	94	93	92	91
90	89	88	87	86	85	84		82	81
80	79	78	77	76		74	73	72	71
70	69	68	67		65	64	63	62	61
60	59	58	57	56	55	54	53	52	
50	49		47	46	45	44	43	42	41
40		38	37	36	35	34	33	32	31
30	29	28	27	26	25	24	23	22	
20	19	18	17		15	14	13	12	11
10	9	8	7	6	5	4		2	1

Learn Together

Cover up other numbers on the **100-chart**, encouraging your child to count backward and identify the missing numbers. With your child, create **number lines** to use for other simple problems.

Super Frames

How many blobs of goo are flying at Mr. Incredible?

Draw 23 squishy blobs of goo.

Circle groups of 10 blobs.

There are _____ groups of 10 blobs

with another _____ blobs.

Represent your blobs of goo in these 10-frames.

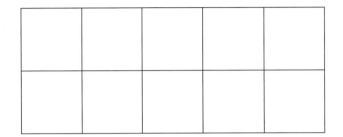

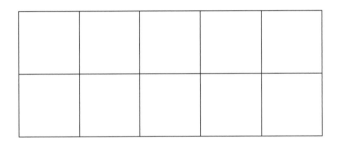

Represent 23 another way.

The Greatest

These racers know that order is important.

In each box, which number is **greater**?

(Circle) the greater number.

Use 10-frames to help you.

| 29 26 | 18 11 | 24 30 | 21 19 |

Mark each pair of numbers on the number line.

(Circle) the number that is **greater**.

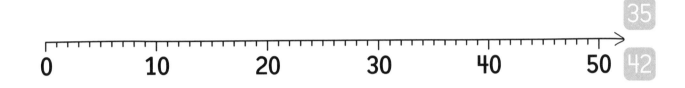

35
42

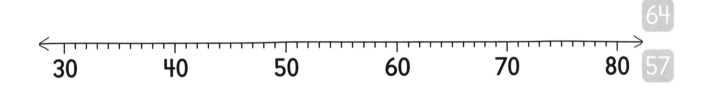

64
57

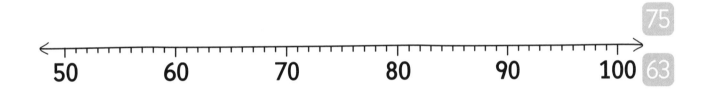

75
63

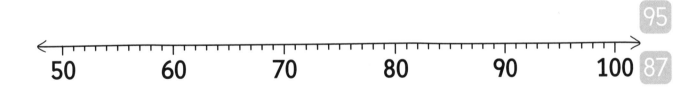

95
87

Learn Together Use 10-frames or number lines to help your child put number sets in order from least to greatest (87, 65, 70; 82, 98, 86; 68, 83, 100). As they master sets of three, introduce a fourth number to each set.

We're Rich!

Woody and Buzz are counting money.

Draw a line from each coin to how much it is worth.

$2

5¢

$1

10¢

25¢

Show **25¢** in **2** ways.

Show **50¢** in **2** ways.

Show **$1** in **2** ways.

Learn Together

Work with your child to figure out other ways to show these amounts. Use coins to help them.

Just a Fraction

The Omnidroid can break whole objects apart!

A part of a whole is called a **fraction**.

When there are **2** equal parts,
we call each part a **half**.

One half can be shown as $\frac{1}{2}$.

Colour **half** of each shape below.
The first one has been done for you.

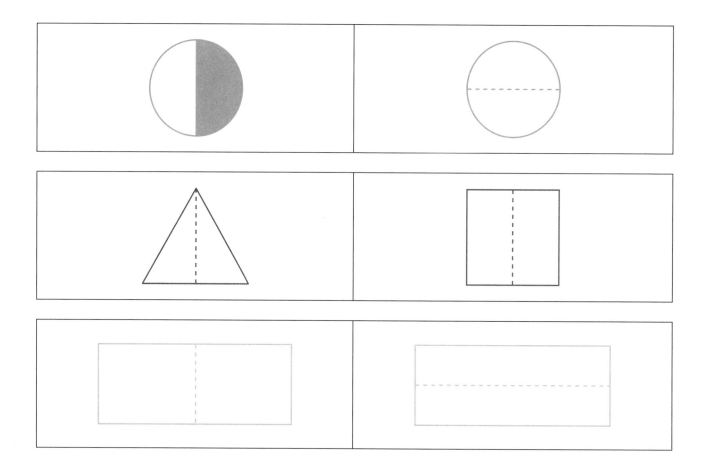

When there are 4 equal parts, we call each part a **fourth** or a **quarter**.

One quarter can be shown as $\frac{1}{4}$.

Colour one **fourth** of each shape below.

The first one has been done for you.

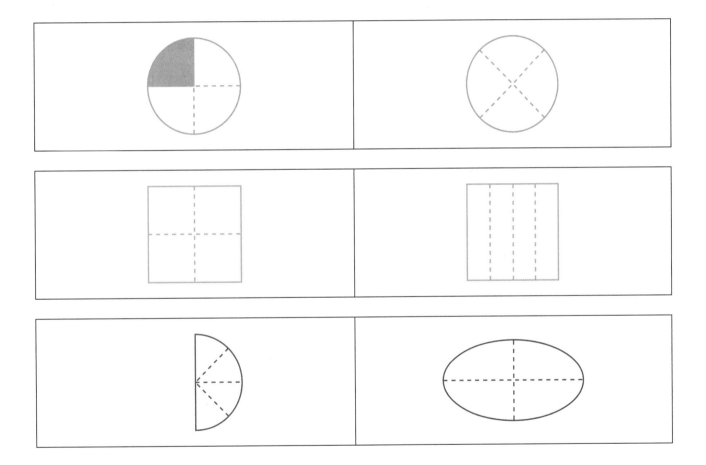

Part of a Whole

Riley and her family need to share each dish into three equal parts.

When there are **3** equal parts, we call each part a **third**.

One third can be shown as $\frac{1}{3}$.

Colour **one third** of each shape.

The first one has been done for you.

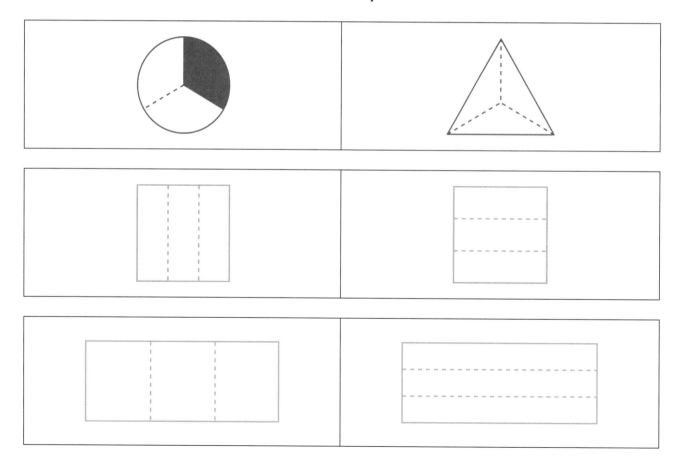

This bar is **8** blocks long.

Split the bar in **half**.

How many blocks are in each half? _____

This bar is 4 blocks long.

Split the bar in **fourths**.

How many blocks are in each fourth? _____

This bar is 9 blocks long.

Split the bar in **thirds**.

How many blocks are in each third? _____

Learn Together — Repeat this activity using different numbers of blocks.

Over and Over

Patterns repeat over and over.
Spot the pattern in this picture.

Draw the part of each pattern
that repeats over and over.

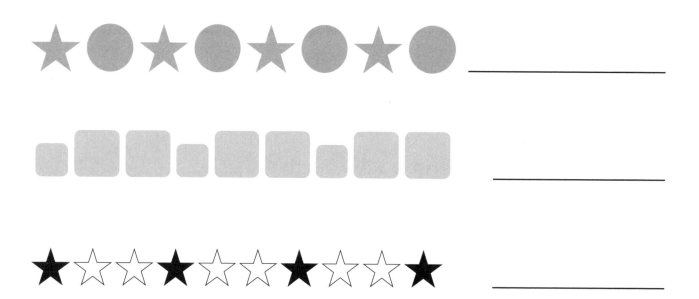

ABA ABA ABA ABA _____

Describe one of the patterns above.

_____

Patterns can change by size, shape, colour, or direction.

Draw the part of each pattern that repeats.

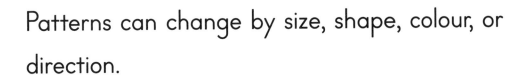

ABcD ABcD ABcD ABcD _____

Describe one of the patterns above.

_____

107

Colourful Patterns

What patterns do you see
in this picture?

Finish each of the patterns
below by adding colour.

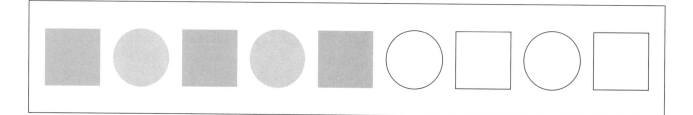

Choose **2** shapes and **2** colours to make a pattern.

Draw your pattern.

Now choose **3** shapes and **3** colours to make a pattern.

Draw your pattern.

Learn Together

Look for patterns in your home (tiles or wallpaper, or how the table is set: fork, plate, glass, fork, plate, glass). Encourage your child to describe the pattern and continue it.

Growing and Shrinking

Extend each pattern.

(Circle) if the pattern
is **shrinking** or **growing**.

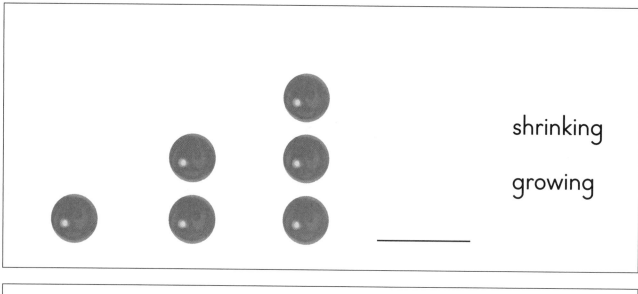

shrinking

growing

_____

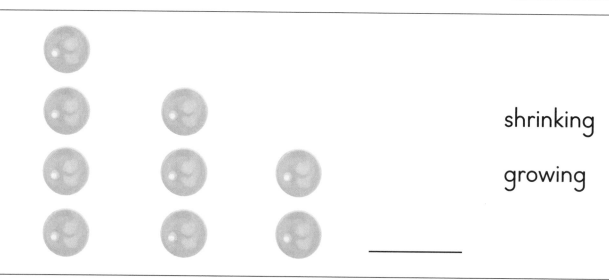

shrinking

growing

_____

Extend each pattern.

(Circle) if the pattern is **shrinking** or **growing**.

5 10 15 20 25 30 ____

shrinking

growing

EEEEE EEEE EEE ____

shrinking

growing

32 30 28 26 24 22 ____

shrinking

growing

Learn Together   With your child, create shrinking and growing patterns for each other to extend.

111

Skipping Along

<u>　5　</u>　　　 _____　　　 _____　　　 _____

Each bookshelf can hold 5 books.

Skip count by 5s.

How many books are there in total? _____

Hamm holds 4 quarters.

Skip count by 25s.

<u>25¢</u>　　　 _____　　　 _____　　　 _____

How much money is there in total? _____

Use a number line to help you skip count.

This number line shows skip counting by 5s.

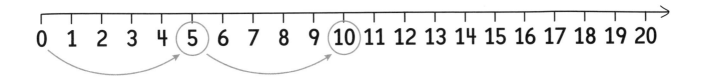

Find the next 3 numbers.

5, 7, _____ , _____ , _____

10, 12, _____ , _____ , _____

3, 6, _____ , _____ , _____

4, 8, _____ , _____ , _____

 **Learn Together** Make your own number lines to help your child skip count.

It All Adds Up

How many times do Fluke and Rudder bark at Gerald?

3 + 6 = ☐   9 + 9 = ☐

4 + 2 = ☐   11 + 5 = ☐

7 + 10 = ☐   4 + 8 = ☐

                         14 + 2 = ☐

Look at the 10-frames.

Write the addition sentences.

⬜ + ⬜ = ⬜

⬜ + ⬜ = ⬜

⬜ + ⬜ = ⬜

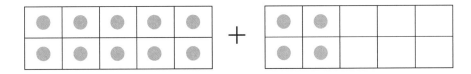

Learn Together

Use toy cars or other objects to recreate the equations on page 114. Create other problems for your child to solve using the toys. Encourage them to record the problem using an **addition sentence**.

How Many?

19 friends help Dory escape.

1 Dory and 19 friends

is [ ]

Find each sum.

You can use counters to help you.

The **sum** is the answer to an addition sentence.

11 + 9 = [ ]   6 + 14 = [ ]

19 + 1 = [ ]   9 + 11 = [ ]

What do you notice about the sums?

_____

Find each sum.

You can use counters to help you.

12 + 8 = ▢   15 + 5 = ▢

3 + 17 = ▢   5 + 15 = ▢

What do you notice about the sums?

_____

Write another addition sentence that fits
with the ones above.

Adding Nothing

Read this addition story.

7 friends are playing a game.
No other friends want to play.
How many friends are playing the game?

This addition story can be written as an addition sentence.

7 + 0 = 7

Find each sum.

20 + 0 = [ ]   0 + 11 = [ ]

12 + 0 = [ ]   17 + 0 = [ ]

What do you notice when you add **0** to a number?

_____

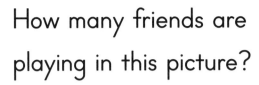

How many friends are playing in this picture?

No one joins them.

Write the addition sentence for this story.

◻ + ◻ = ◻

Find each sum.

18 + 0 = ◻   0 + 25 = ◻

31 + 0 = ◻   0 + 14 = ◻

49 + 0 = ◻   50 + 0 = ◻

Solve It!

The Incredibles know how to solve problems.

How do you solve two-digit addition problems?

You can solve $10 + 14$ using a 50-chart.

Find 14 on the 50-chart. Jump forward 10 to get 24.

1	2	3	4	5	6	7	8	9	10
11	12	13	14	15	16	17	18	19	20
21	22	23	24	25	26	27	28	29	30
31	32	33	34	35	36	37	38	39	40
41	42	43	44	45	46	47	48	49	50

You can also solve 10 + 14 by making friendly numbers.

10 + 14

10 + 10 + 4 = 24

So, 10 + 14 = 24

Find each sum.

13 + 10 = ☐   15 + 10 = ☐

16 + 10 = ☐   17 + 10 = ☐

20 + 10 = ☐   20 + 13 = ☐

20 + 15 = ☐   20 + 20 = ☐

20 + 21 = ☐   20 + 22 = ☐

Learn Together
Your child may use various strategies to solve these problems, including using a 50-chart, interconnecting blocks, or counters on 10-frames. Discuss the strategies they are using.

Add That Cash

Money is kept in cash registers.

Look at the coins.

Write **addition sentences**.

Figure out how much money there is in total.

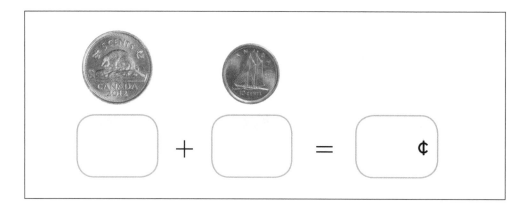

[ ] + [ ] = [ ] ¢

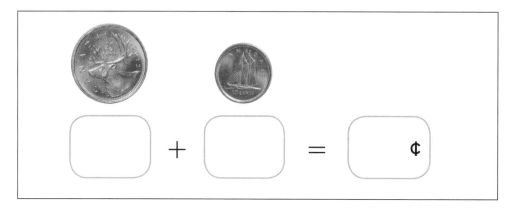

[ ] + [ ] = [ ] ¢

Look at the coins.

Estimate, then find the total.

Estimate   Total

Estimate   Total

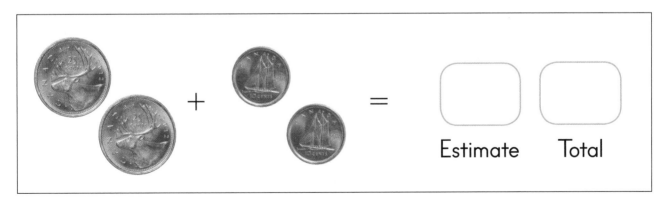

Estimate   Total

Learn Together

Your child might use real coins to help them with these addition problems. Provide them with similar problems to practise **estimating** and adding.

I "Otter" Take Some Away

There are 12 otters.

Some of the otters dive under the water.

How many are left?

Write the **subtraction sentence**.

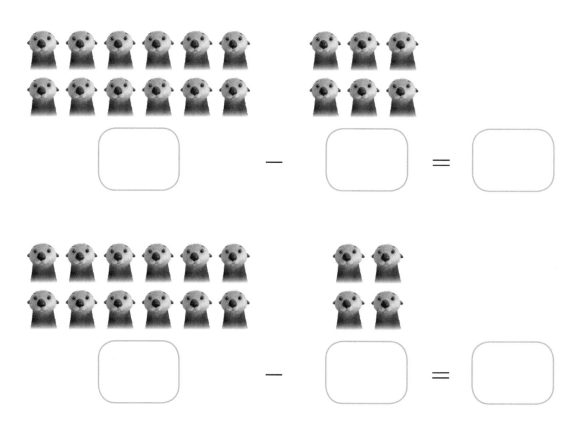

⬜ − ⬜ = ⬜

⬜ − ⬜ = ⬜

Look at the 10-frames.

Write the subtraction sentences.

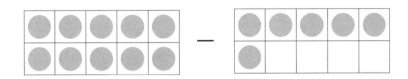

$$\bigcirc - \bigcirc = \bigcirc$$

$$\bigcirc - \bigcirc = \bigcirc$$

$$\bigcirc - \bigcirc = \bigcirc$$

Learn Together

Create other **subtraction sentences** for your child to solve by covering these 10-frames with counters (buttons, blocks).

What's Left?

There are 4 toys all together.

Then 1 toy falls.

How many are left?

$4 - 1 = \boxed{}$

Subtract to find each difference.

The **difference** is the answer to a subtraction sentence.

$9 - 1 = \boxed{}$ $7 - 3 = \boxed{}$

$14 - 1 = \boxed{}$ $8 - 3 = \boxed{}$

$18 - 4 = \boxed{}$ $12 - 4 = \boxed{}$

$17 - 4 = \boxed{}$ $16 - 4 = \boxed{}$

There are 5 toys all together.

1 toy leaves.

How many are left?

$5 - 1 = $ ☐

Subtract to find each difference.

$18 - 2 = $ ☐ $20 - 2 = $ ☐

$18 - 3 = $ ☐ $20 - 3 = $ ☐

$18 - 4 = $ ☐ $24 - 4 = $ ☐

$18 - 5 = $ ☐ $25 - 5 = $ ☐

Learn Together Make subtraction part of everyday activities. How many bananas are left when we eat 1 for breakfast? When we clean 4 dirty dishes, how many dirty dishes are left?

Take Away Nothing!

Read this subtraction story.

Riley has 5 emotions. Riley needs all her emotions.

None of the emotions should be blocked.

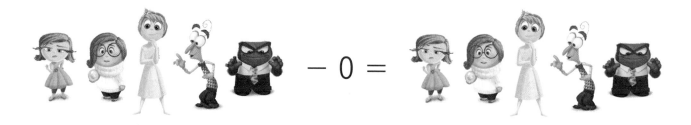

Solve these subtraction sentences.

18 − 0 = [　]   10 − 0 = [　]

11 − 0 = [　]   17 − 0 = [　]

What do you notice when you subtract **0** from a number?

_____

Solve these subtraction sentences.

Use counters or 10-frames to help you.

17 − 1 = ☐   16 − 5 = ☐

13 − 3 = ☐   12 − 3 = ☐

15 − 4 = ☐   19 − 6 = ☐

18 − 0 = ☐   11 − 1 = ☐

20 − 5 = ☐   14 − 4 = ☐

16 − 3 = ☐   18 − 5 = ☐

12 − 4 = ☐   15 − 0 = ☐

Learn Together With your child, create another **subtraction story** for the image on page 130 or another image.

All Gone!

There are 25 fish on the reef.

How many are left when 10 fish leave?

You can solve 25 - 10 using a 50-chart.

Find 25 on the 50-chart. Jump back 10 to get 15.

1	2	3	4	5	6	7	8	9	10
11	12	13	14	15	16	17	18	19	20
21	22	23	24	25	26	27	28	29	30
31	32	33	34	35	36	37	38	39	40
41	42	43	44	45	46	47	48	49	50

Find each difference.

22 − 10 = ⬜

23 − 10 = ⬜

24 − 10 = ⬜

26 − 10 = ⬜

29 − 10 = ⬜

38 − 20 = ⬜

40 − 10 = ⬜

43 − 10 = ⬜

45 − 10 = ⬜

50 − 10 = ⬜

33 − 20 = ⬜

38 − 20 = ⬜

40 − 30 = ⬜

44 − 30 = ⬜

Learn Together

Discuss any patterns your child notices in some of their answers (subtracting 10 from a number means the first digit in the first two-digit number is one less than it was before). They can use those patterns to help them develop strategies for solving problems.

Less Cash

Look at the coins.

Figure out how much money is

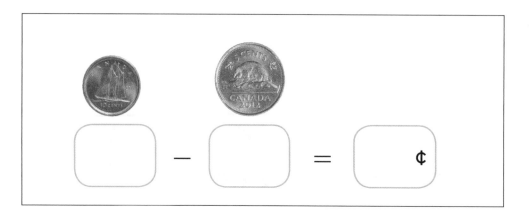

Look at the coins.

Figure out how much money is left.

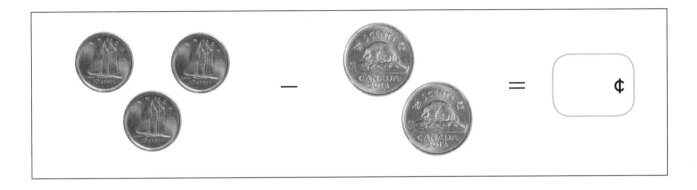

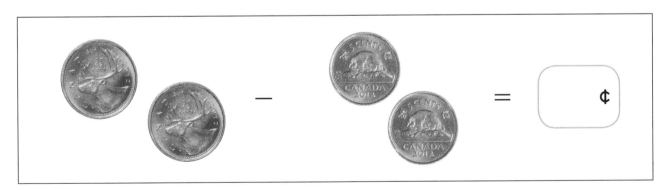

Learn Together Help your child use real coins to make their calculations. Pose other subtraction problems for them to solve.

Adding Up and Taking Away

The otters are happy to have Dory for a friend!

If you know that

4 otters + 1 Dory = 5 friends,

then you know that 5 − 1 = 4.

Use the addition sentences to help you solve the related subtraction sentences.

8 + 5 = 13   13 − 5 = ☐

5 + 6 = 11   11 − 5 = ☐

9 + 8 = 17   17 − 8 = ☐

7 + 9 = 16   16 − 9 = ☐

Use the subtraction sentences to help you solve the related addition sentences.

$14 - 8 = 6$ $8 + 6 = \boxed{}$

$16 - 6 = 10$ $6 + 10 = \boxed{}$

$18 - 7 = 11$ $7 + 11 = \boxed{}$

$17 - 8 = 9$ $8 + 9 = \boxed{}$

$15 - 5 = 10$ $5 + 10 = \boxed{}$

$13 - 8 = 5$ $8 + 5 = \boxed{}$

$11 - 6 = 5$ $6 + 5 = \boxed{}$

Learn Together

Help your child to see how each addition sentence is related to a subtraction sentence, and vice versa. Use blocks or toys to show the relationship for one set of sentences.

Quick Calculations

Can you be as fast as Dash?

What can you add or subtract to change the first number into the final number?

The first one is done for you.

20 − 2 = 18   7   18

8   19   17   11

12   3   20   25

5   15   16   4

7   5

11   15

9   17

16   12

25   20

8   4

20   10

24   12

13   21

22   25

15   9

14   21

8   14

10   20

Learn Together

Your child can use 10-frames to picture each problem. If they need a hint, tell them to first figure out if the answer is increasing (addition) or decreasing (subtraction).

Joining Equal Groups

You **multiply** when you join equal groups.

Here are **4** groups of **2** fish.

There are **8** fish altogether.

4 × 2 = 8

> This is another way to show the word multiply.

Here are ⬜ groups of ⬜ fish.

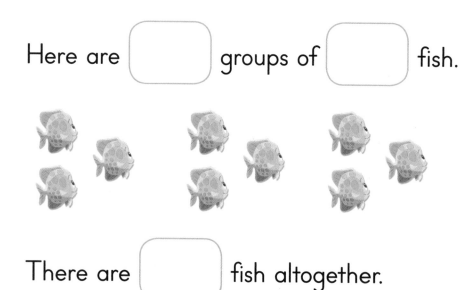

There are ⬜ fish altogether.

Here are ☐ groups of ☐ fish.

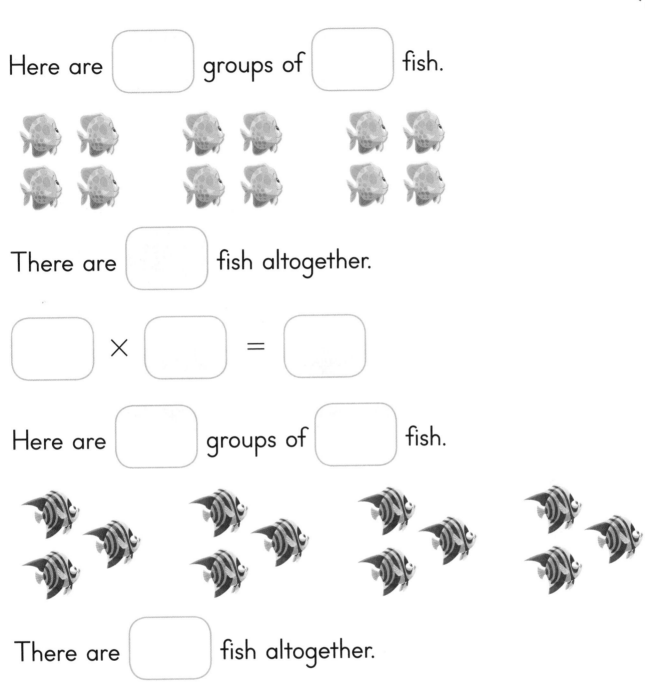

There are ☐ fish altogether.

☐ × ☐ = ☐

Here are ☐ groups of ☐ fish.

There are ☐ fish altogether.

☐ × ☐ = ☐

Learn Together

As your child is being introduced to multiplication, they will still be counting the items within each group to reach a total. Using concrete objects to help them with multiplication is part of this early learning.

Let's Multiply

Flo has many barrels of oil.

You can multiply to find out how many she has.

There are **3** groups of **2** barrels.

There are **6** barrels all together.

$3 \times 2 = 6$

There are **2** groups of **3** barrels.

$2 \times 3 = \boxed{}$

There are **6** groups of **2** barrels.

$6 \times 2 = $ ☐

There are **7** groups of **2** barrels.

$7 \times 2 = $ ☐

There are **3** groups of **3** barrels.

$3 \times 3 = $ ☐

Learn Together

Provide your child with other simple scenarios to practise multiplying. Say, "Let's multiply as we set the table. We need 3 sets of 4: 4 plates, 4 knives, and 4 forks. $3 \times 4 = 12$.

Counting Groups

Edna Mode buys lots of masks for the Supers.

How many masks are there?

(Circle) every group of **2** masks.

Fill in the boxes.

$$2 + 2 + 2 + 2 + 2 + \boxed{} = \boxed{}$$

There are $\boxed{}$ groups of 2.

$$\boxed{} \times 2 = \boxed{}$$

There are $\boxed{}$ masks.

More masks just arrived!

How many masks are there?

(Circle) every group of **3** masks.

Fill in the boxes.

3 + 3 + 3 + ⬚ = ⬚

There are ⬚ groups of 3.

⬚ × 3 = ⬚

There are ⬚ masks.

Separating Equal Groups

You **divide** when you want to share a group in equal parts.

1 race car has 4 tires.

How many race cars share **8** tires?

race cars.

How many race cars share **12** tires?

 race cars.

How many race cars share **16** tires?

[ ] race cars.

How many race cars share **20** tires?

[ ] race cars.

How many race cars share **24** tires?

[ ] race cars.

Learn Together

Your child is just being introduced to the concept of division. Help your child solve these problems. Provide them with counters to arrange into groups of 4.

Mission Division

Sarge has 12 Green Army Men.

He needs to send them on 2 different missions.

He can **divide** them equally to find out how many to send on each mission.

This is another way to show the word divide.

12 ÷ 2 = 6

Circle groups of Green Army Men to show
each division sentence

12 ÷ 6 = ☐

12 ÷ 3 = ☐

12 ÷ 4 = ☐

Learn Together
Use objects like beads to find the answers and create other problems to solve. The idea of sharing is a familiar one for children, and can help them understand how one group might be divided into smaller equal groups.

Making Equal Groups

Show how the 10 fish below can be divided equally into 2 parts of the reef.

Each part of the reef has  fish.

You have 20 marbles.

Fill each box with an equal number of marbles to show each division sentence..

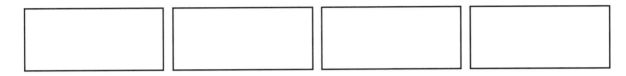

20 ÷ 4 = ☐

20 ÷ 5 = ☐

20 ÷ 10 = ☐

Learn Together Help your child figure out how to fill the boxes. Ask, "Is there another way to share the marbles equally?" (2 boxes with 10 marbles each; 20 boxes with 1 marble each).

Measure It!

Who is taller, Sadness or Joy?

You can measure people and objects to find out exactly how tall they are.

You can use centimetres to measure how tall you are. A **centimetre** is a unit of measure.

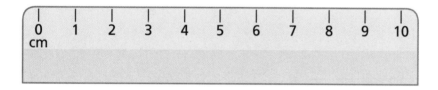

The symbol for a centimetre is **cm**.

This domino is 3 cm long.

This crayon is 9 cm long.

Use a ruler to measure these items.

My thumb is about _____ cm long.

My hand is about _____ cm long.

My arm is about _____ cm long.

My foot is about _____ cm long.

My pencil is about _____ cm long.

My favourite book is about _____ cm long.

My favourite toy is about _____ cm long.

Learn Together

If your child is using a ruler for the first time, they will need help to understand how to use it. They can measure other items using a ruler or tape measure. Discuss the terms *length*, *width*, and *height* and how they differ.

Incredibly Far

You can use metres to measure how far Elastigirl can run. A **metre** is a unit of measure.

A metre is 100 centimetres long.

The symbol for metres is **m**.

Draw something that is about 1 metre long.

(Circle) the unit of measurement that is most appropriate to measure the giraffe and the girl.

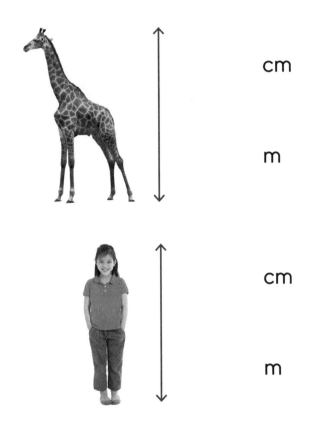

cm

m

cm

m

How tall are you?

I am about _____ cm tall.

I am about _____ m tall.

Learn Together

Help your child measure their height. Measure other objects using centimetres and metres.

Hold It!

Fillmore wants to know which containers hold about the **same**.

(Circle) the objects in each row that hold about the **same**.

Estimate how many glasses of water
each container will hold.

(Circle) the container that holds the **most**.

Container	Estimate	Actual Measurement
pitcher		
pot		
pan		

Heavy or Light?

It's the Incredible family!

Who do you think
is the **heaviest**?

(Circle) the object in each pair that is **heavier**.

You can use a pan balance to compare the mass of two objects.

If you put two objects on a pan balance, how do you know which one is lighter?

_____

_____

_____

_____

_____

Learn Together

Help your child compare the mass of objects using a pan balance, or a kitchen or bathroom scale. Note that your child may not yet have been introduced to units of measurement for mass.

How Big?

Estimate the number of squares that cover
this picture.

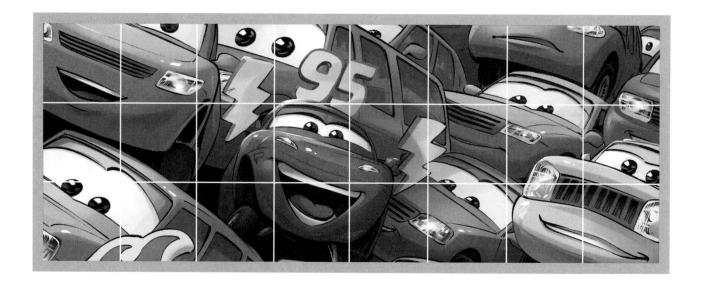

Now count the number of squares that cover
the picture.

You figured out the **area** of the picture. **Area**
is the amount of space inside of a shape.

Estimate the area of this rectangle.

Count the squares.

The area is _____ squares.

Estimate the area of this rectangle.

Count the squares.

The area is _____ squares.

Estimate the area of this rectangle.

Count the squares.

The area is _____ squares.

Learn Together
Work with your child to find the area of other objects. Use different items to cover the surface (cubes, blocks) and compare the area of each surface.

Counting the Days

Woody is interested in the calendar on Andy's wall.

Arrange these in order from **shortest** to **longest**.

month   week   year   day

How many months are in **1** year? ☐

How many days are in **1** week? ☐

Some months have 31 days.

Some months have 30 days.

February has 28 days, except every 4 years it has 29.

Put the month and numbers (or dates) on this calendar.

Month: _____

Sunday	Monday	Tuesday	Wednesday	Thursday	Friday	Saturday

Put a star on today's date.

How many days until the end of the month? ⬜

Learn Together

Help your child complete the calendar above for the current month. Plan activities using the calendar. Discuss how many days, or weeks, are left until certain events will occur.

Time Enough

It's time for Riley to go to bed.

Match each clock to the

correct time.

8:45

8:15

8:00

8:30

Show the time you wake up.

Show the time you eat lunch.

Show the time you go to bed.

Learn Together Your child is just beginning to understand the concept of time. Practise telling time together and talk about time ("It's five o'clock. Do you want to help me get dinner ready?" "It's 7:30, half an hour to your bedtime.").

Shaping Up

Hank can see many shapes when he escapes his tank.

What shapes do you see in this picture?

Complete the table below.

Shape	Draw the Shape	Number of Sides
square		
rectangle		
triangle		
circle		

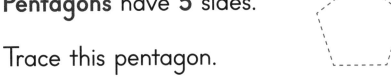

Pentagons have **5** sides.

Trace this pentagon.

Now, draw your own pentagon.

(Circle) the pentagons.

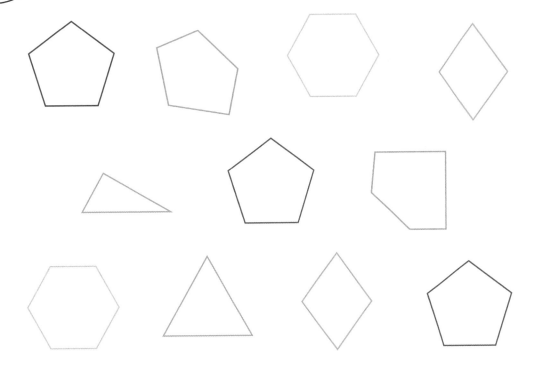

Learn Together With your child, discuss and compare these shapes.

Many Sides

Can you find a hexagon in this picture?

Hexagons have **6** sides.

Trace this hexagon.

Now, draw your own hexagon.

Circle the hexagons.

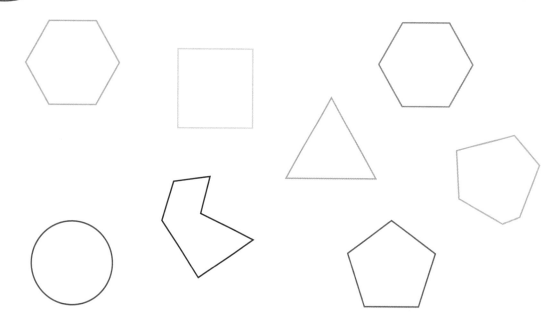

Octagons have **8** sides.

Trace this octagon.

Now, draw your own octagon.

Circle the octagons.

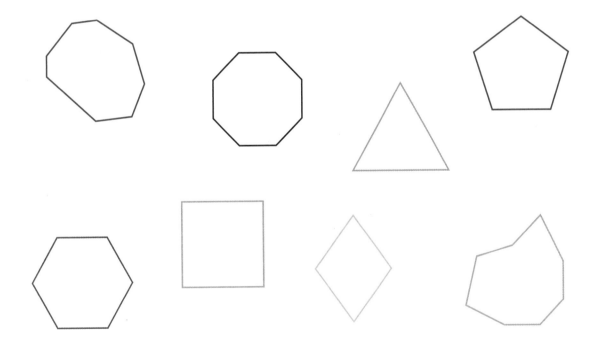

Learn Together With your child, look for shapes in your home. Count the sides. Sort the shapes using a table like the one on page 164. Your child can draw the shape in the first column.

167

All Sorts of Shapes

Woody is trapped in a crate. The crate is made up of a lot of **quadrilaterals**. Quadrilaterals have **4** sides.

Squares, rectangles, diamonds, and rhombuses are all quadrilaterals.

(Circle) the quadrilaterals.

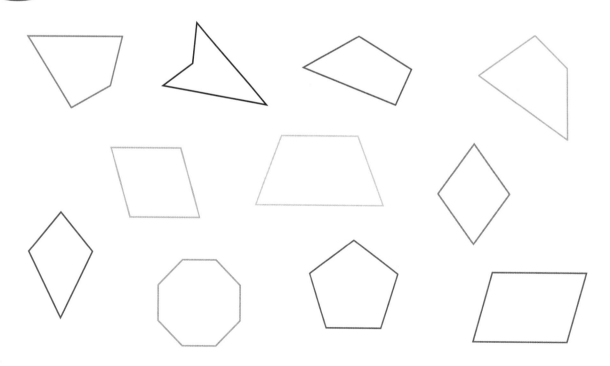

Complete the table below.

Shape	Draw the Shape	Number of Sides
pentagon		
hexagon		
octagon		
quadrilateral		

Learn Together
Encourage your child to practise drawing various shapes. Help them label these shapes.

Shape Fun!

What shapes do you see in this truck?

What shapes make up the truck below? Label the shapes.

Use shapes to create your own truck!

Label your shapes.

Power Objects

(Circle) the 3-D objects you see in this picture.

Use these words to name each 3-D object below.

cube   **cone**   **cylinder**   **sphere**

 _____

(cube) _____

 _____

 _____

Name one of the 3-D objects you circled in the picture.

_____

Use the clues to answer these riddles.

All my faces are the same and I have 8 vertices.

What am I? _____

I have one vertex and can roll.

What am I? _____

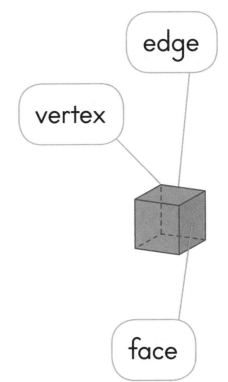

edge

vertex

face

I have flat faces and can be stacked.

What am I? _____

I have no vertices and can roll.

What am I? _____

Learn Together

Help your child create other riddles for 3-D objects. Your child can create 3-D objects using modelling clay or other materials. They can describe and label the objects.

In 3-D

What 3-D objects do you see in this picture?

Pyramids and **prisms** are also 3-D objects.

Use these words to name each 3-D object below.

triangular prism   cone pyramid
rectangular prism

 _____

 _____

 _____

Use the clues to
answer these riddles.

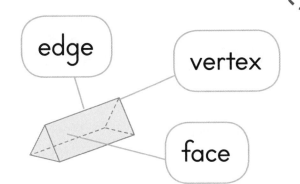

I have six faces and can stack.

What am I? _____

I have five faces and five vertices.

What am I? _____

I have two triangular faces and three rectangular faces.

What am I? _____

Write another riddle for one 3-D object.

_____

Learn Together Talk about how some shapes can roll and some shapes can stack (and some can do both). Use blocks or other objects to experiment to find out which 3-D objects are best for stacking and rolling.

Find Your Way

Dory needs to find her parents.

When you need to find something, you might use a **map**.

Examine the map below.

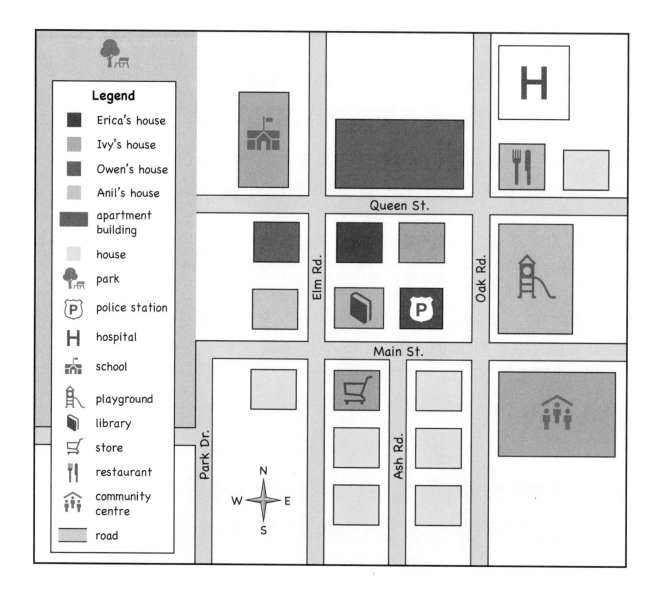

Start at Erica's house.

Walk east along Queen Street.

Turn north on Oak Road. Walk to the end of the street.

Where are you? _____

Write directions from the hospital to the store.

_____

_____

_____

Write directions from the community centre to the library.

_____

_____

What Are the Chances?

Jackson Storm

Chuck Armstrong

Lightning McQueen

Manny Flywheel

Cruz Ramirez

Look at the picture.

Circle the word that best describes each statement.

Lightning McQueen will win the race.

likely   unlikely   certain   impossible

Chuck Armstrong will win the race.

likely   unlikely   certain   impossible

Manny Flywheel will win the race.

likely   unlikely   certain   impossible

Chuck Armstrong will finish the race before
Jackson Storm.

likely   unlikely   certain   impossible

This race will have a winner.

likely   unlikely   certain   impossible

Write your own probability statement
about the race.

_____

_____

Learn Together
Discuss the meaning of each **probability** phrase with your child. Encourage them to use one of these phrases as they write a new statement. Play games with spinners or dice to help your child learn about probability.

Picturing Numbers

A **bar graph** uses bars to show **data**.

How Riley Feels

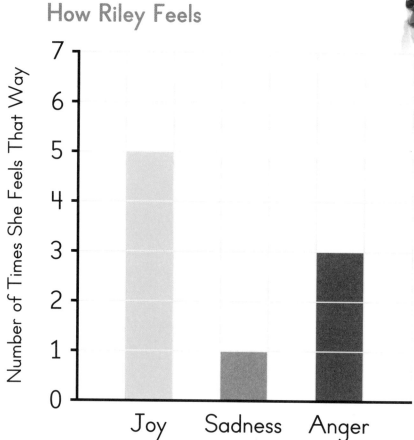

Riley feels Joy [ ] times.

She feels Sadness [ ] time.

She feels Anger [ ] times.

Create a bar graph to show
how you felt yesterday.

I felt joy _____ times.

I felt sadness _____ times.

I felt anger _____ times.

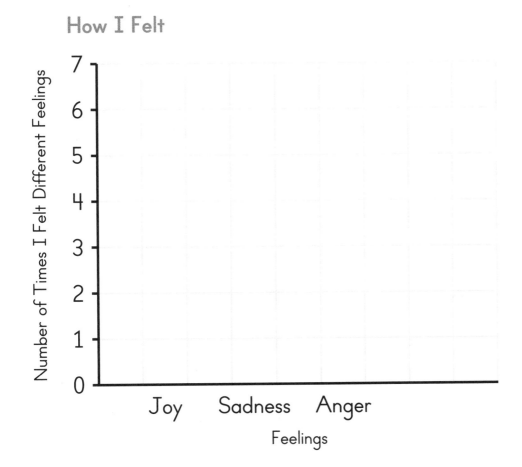

How I Felt

Learn Together Help your child complete the graph. They may want to add more bars for other emotions (embarrassed, proud, frustrated).

Graph Up

Woody asks his friends what colour he should paint the house.

Their paint colour choices are on this **line plot**.

A **line plot** uses an x to show how many times something happened.

House Paint Colours

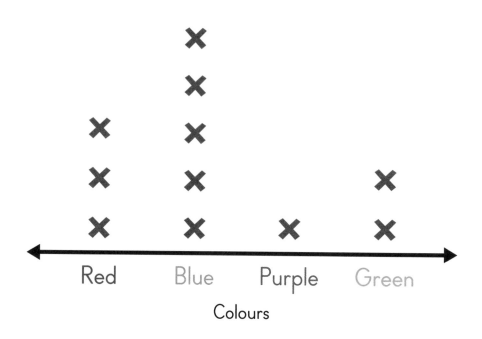

How many friends want the house to be blue? _____

Create a line plot.

Show the favourite ice cream flavours

of your family or friends.

Favourite Ice Cream Flavours

Vanilla   Chocolate   Strawberry

Flavours

What does your line plot tell you? _____

_____

What's Next?

As your child completes the topics in this book, extend their learning with some of the following activities.

Letter Recognition

- Help your child arrange objects in alphabetical order.

- Together, sort books into alphabetical order on your child's bookshelf. Decide whether it will be alphabetical by title or author's last name.

- At the store, encourage your child to look at how the spices are organized (usually in alphabetical order). Name a spice for them to find. Take turns finding spices you each name.

- Your child is surrounded by environmental print. Examples include signs, labels, maps, and advertising. Encourage them to read environmental print, praising their growing reading ability.

Word Knowledge

- Your child can highlight word patterns they see in these activities (such as the long *o* sound in *road, boat, soap*; adding *-ed* to some verbs to make the past tense). They can begin a word knowledge notebook for word patterns and word families.

- As your child's reading skills develop, they will notice many exceptions to general rules (the *ei* in *eight* makes a long *a* sound, not a long *e* sound; past tense of *swim* is *swam*, not *swimmed*). Challenge them to add these rules and exceptions to their word knowledge notebook.

- Use fridge magnets or flash cards to create word families (short vowel: *-ad, -at, -et, ed*; long vowel: *-ape, -aid, -eet, -eed*). Your child can experiment with adding consonants to make words (dad, pad, mad, sad; deed, seed, feed).

- Create a three-column chart for nouns—person, place, thing. Give your child a minute to list as many nouns as they can think of.

- Together, play a game of charades. Take turns acting out a verb.

Comprehension

- As you read or watch shows, ask your child questions to help them make predictions and inferences. ("Riley is unhappy about moving. What do you think she's going to do?")

- Encourage your child's questions about stories and nonfiction text.

- Use wordless picture books to help your child practise making inferences and drawing conclusions.

- To practise making inferences, play Paper Bag Mysteries. Add some clues about a familiar character to a paper bag. Your child can remove the clues one by one and start to make inferences about who the character is.

- The classic game of Twenty Questions requires your child to make inferences.

- As you read the title of a book, ask: "What do you think the story is about? Who is the main character? Do you think the story will be happy, sad, or something else? Why?"

- Your child will still need support identifying the main idea. As you watch movies together, discuss the main idea. Challenge them to summarize the movie.

- Pictures help your child make sense of text. Encourage your child to examine the pictures closely to understand what has happened, where a story is set, or how characters are feeling.

Writing

- Create a mystery message together for someone else to read—omit the first letter of each word.

- Create sentence starters for your child to finish. ("I want a ____. Do you want to go to the _____? I love _____.")

- Create a digital photo album together, with photos of your child's life. They can write simple captions.

- With your child, write stories, lists, letters, poems, and other texts.

- Write notes to one another and leave them in secret places.

- Together, create a treasure map for your child to follow.

- Your child can write labels or captions for their drawings.

- As your child writes using various verb tenses, encourage them to say the sentence to figure out form and spelling. Look for patterns that can help them (ending some verbs with -ed) and for exceptions to rules (ate/eat; got/get; went/go) that they can add to their word knowledge notebook.

- What kind of superheroes would you and your child like to be? Draw pictures of yourselves as superheroes. Label the parts of your costumes and write captions for your pictures.

What's Next?

Number Sense

- Using 100 small objects, make number groups (40 objects, 60 objects). Your child can write the number and the word for that number.

- Create 10-frame boxes to help your child count objects. Create a hundreds chart and provide your child with 100 counters (buttons, beads) to cover it to help them with addition and subtraction.

- Invite your child to help you cook and bake. Point out how many recipes use fractions. Can they figure out how much of each ingredient is needed?

- Count backwards from 100 together, pausing now and then to let your child fill in the number.

Collecting and Using Data

- Play games that include an element of probability (any game that includes dice, spinners, or cards).

- Discuss the outcome of events using phrases such as *unlikely*, *certain*, and *impossible*.

- Look for graphs and tables as you read nonfiction texts together. Ask questions about the graphs and tables.

Patterns

- Encourage your child to sort objects, such as toys, by providing them with bins or other containers. Talk about the rules they are using to sort. ("All of the red toys went in the red bin. Are you sorting by colour?")

- Your child can sort their laundry as they put it away. What rule will they use?

- Mix some objects into a bin (pens, toys, spoons). What rule will your child use to sort the objects?

- As you take out or put away seasonal decorations, allow your child to help sort the objects (by colour, purpose, material, size, and so on).

- Look for patterns in nature and around your home.

- Give your child objects to create patterns with (blocks, buttons, school supplies, toys).

- Create a pattern and ask your child to add to it. Ask your child to create a pattern for you to finish.

Addition and Subtraction

- With your child, create a number line from zero to 100. Give them groups of objects to add and subtract.

- Play games involving skip counting ("hide and seek" with the searcher counting to 100 by 2s). Skip count by 2s, 5s, and 10s together.

- Use connecting blocks to make counting cubes (1s, 10s, and 100s) for solving problems. ("If I have 32 blocks and 23 blocks, how many blocks do I have altogether?").

- Look for natural sets in your home that can be used for problems involving multiplication and division (two cases of juice boxes; 12 cans of soup).

- When you shop, provide opportunities to multiply and divide. Say, "If we need three apples a day for five days, how many apples do we need? This pizza has 12 pieces, and 4 people will eat it. How many pieces does each person get?"

Measurement

- Encourage your child to compare the length, width, or height of various items. Ask: "Is your glass taller than a pencil? Is your book wider than a favourite toy?"

- Use your cellphone to look for geocaches in your neighbourhood. Your child will enjoy the adventure of finding hidden objects as they learn how to follow directions and navigate.

- With your child, talk about the timing of events. "Next Wednesday, we'll go swimming at seven o'clock. But that means we'll need to eat half an hour earlier. What time should we eat?"

Geometry

- Look for 3-D objects in your home, noting their shapes (cans are cylinders). Your child can draw and label the objects and shapes.

- Look for shapes as you take a walk in your neighbourhood. ("That door is a rectangle. The window is a square.")

- Look for 3-D objects in your neighbourhood. If possible, let your child examine and touch all the sides.

- Look for maps as you are out with your child—in shopping malls, parks, and bus stations. Examine the maps together.

- Use position words to describe the location of places.

Glossary

100-chart a table that displays the numbers from 1 to 100 (or 0 to 99). This chart can be a useful tool for your child when skip counting, adding, or subtracting.

10-frames two-by-five rectangle frames used to help teach counting. Counters are placed to illustrate numbers less than or equal to ten.

addition sentence a number sentence or equation used to express addition (4 + 1 = 5).

addition stories one or more statements that illustrate a math addition equation. For example, the equation 2 + 2 = 4 could be told as a story about two children who are joined by two friends.

alphabetical order to arrange words according to the order of letters in the alphabet.

arrays to arrange items in rows or columns to make it easier to count or calculate totals.

background knowledge what your child knows of the world—information that can help them as they read. As they read stories, they connect to that knowledge to help them make sense of text. Your child will use background knowledge to make predictions, make inferences, and draw conclusions.

chart (or table) a graphic organizer used to sort and organize information in ways that make it easier to read, compare it, and understand it.

compound word a word composed of two or more smaller words (background). Your child can sometimes use their knowledge of the smaller words to figure out the meaning of the compound word.

consonant blends two or more consonants that work together in a word, where each consonant can be distinctly heard (the *s* in *snake* or the *ft* in *raft*).

context the words or text surrounding an unfamiliar word that can be used to help clarify the meaning of that word.

contractions words created by joining two words using an apostrophe to replace the missing letters (don't, I'm, you're).

digraphs two consonants working together in a word to make one sound (the *sh* in *shake* or the *ck* in *block*).

drawing conclusions to make decisions about or evaluations of the events or characters in stories. This reading strategy supports your child's understanding of texts, but also requires them to apply critical thinking skills that are still developing.

estimating to use your understanding of numbers to make an educated guess at an answer to a problem.

fact true information that can be proven or supported. To become a critical reader and thinker, your child will need to differentiate between facts and opinions.

homophone words that sound the same but are spelled differently (to/two/too). It is natural when your child writes for them to still be spelling homophones incorrectly.

make predictions to form an educated guess about what will happen next. This strategy supports your child's understanding of texts.

Glossary

making connections a reading strategy that requires your child to use their background knowledge; this strategy supports your child's understanding of texts. There are three types of connections (text to self, text to text, and text to world).

making inferences to use clues in the text to "read between the lines." This reading strategy requires your child to use their critical thinking skills as well as their background knowledge and understanding of texts.

number line a line showing numbers along it, placed in order. Number lines can help your child as they add, subtract, or think about how one number is related to another (3 comes before 6, 10 is 9 numbers away from 1).

opinion a personal statement or belief. For example, blue is the best colour.

plural words words that indicate there is more than one of something. There are rules, and exceptions to those rules, to follow when making a word plural (baby/babies; child/children; person/people). Your child is just learning these rules as they spell, but will probably already be following the rules when speaking.

prefix letters added to the beginning of a word to change its meaning (return, undone).

probability the chance or likelihood of something happening. Help your child predict the outcome of events (ranging from *impossible* to *certain*) as an introduction to this math concept.

regrouping forming new groups, usually by arranging the ones and tens (or, in higher grades, hundreds and thousands) to understand the total and aid in making calculations.

silent letters letters in a word you do not hear when spoken (*k* in *knife*, *b* in *comb*). Your child is at a stage when they will spell many words as they sound, and not add the silent letters. Encourage them to think about word patterns or families, where appropriate (know, knowledge; when, where, what) or to make up memory aids to remember the spelling ("*B* sure to comb your hair every day.").

skip counting to count in increments other than one (2, 4, 6, 8, 10). Your child will be skip counting by 2s, 5s, and 10s.

story elements characters, setting, and plot are the features of a story. When your child can identify story elements, they develop their understanding and appreciation of the story.

subtraction sentence a number sentence or equation used to express subtraction (4 − 1 + 3).

subtraction stories one or more statements that illustrate a math subtraction equation. For example, the equation 4 − 2 = 2 could be told as a story about four children who are playing, but two friends leave.

suffix letters added to the end of a word to change its meaning (smaller).

verb tenses the varying form of the verb that expresses a time frame—past, present, or future.

verbs action words; note that the spelling rules for verbs can be complex, particularly irregular verbs, which take unusual forms depending on how they are used with other words or in other tenses (eat/ate, am/are/is— for *to be*, go/went, swim/swam).

word ending the letters at the end of a word that form a sound or make the word part of a word family. Your child is using common word endings to help them read new words (fight/right/might; flow/blow/know); knowing how one of these words is pronounced, helps them know how to pronounce other words with the same ending.

word families a group of words related in some way. For example, they begin or end with the same sound (*bed*, *fed*, *red* are part of the *-ed* word family; *black*, *blue*, *blond* are part of the *bl* word family).

Answers

Letter Recognition

Alphabet Blast Attack

The alphabet has been blasted!
What letters are missing?
Fill in the missing capital letters below.

A B C **D** E F G

H **I** J K L **M** N

O P Q **R** S T U

V **W** X Y Z

2

I can identify letters!

What letters are missing?
Fill in the missing lowercase letters below.

a b c **d** e f

g **h** i j k **l** m

n o **p** q r s

t **u** v w x **y** z

3

Letter Recognition

Clean Up the Letters

Can Dory find her parents?
Did you notice that the words in the above sentence are in alphabetical order?
Alphabetical order is when the letters of the alphabet are in the correct sequence.

A B C D E F G H I J K L M N O
P Q R S T U V W X Y Z

Put these words in alphabetical order to make another sentence.

her parents finds Dory
Dory finds her parents.

4

I can sort by alphabetical order!

These letters are in a mess!
Put each group of letters in alphabetical order.
The first one has been done for you.

B D A   Z R M
A B D   **M R Z**

c g e n   x u p k
c e g n   **k p u x**

T w i P   m Y I D
i P T w   **D I m Y**

k a p A   Z s A e
A k p q   **A e s Z**

5

Letter Recognition

Alphabet Rescue!

An Incredible family saves the world!
Did you notice that the words in the above sentence are in alphabetical order?
Put these words in alphabetical order.

fast strong incredible
fast incredible strong

robot hero save
hero robot save

team super mask
mask super team

6

I can put words in alphabetical order!

trick defeat mission
defeat mission trick

island secret beat
beat island secret

home force plane
force home plane

7

Letter Sounds

Lasso Those Letters!

Herd these names into alphabetical order.

Roundup Bullseye Jessie
Bullseye Jessie Roundup

Woody Andy Buzz
Andy Buzz Woody

Sarge Rex Hamm
Hamm Rex Sarge

8

I can put words in alphabetical order!

Put these words in alphabetical order to create a sentence.

Woody Buzz helps
Buzz helps Woody

umbrella the Jessie lassos
Jessie lassos the umbrella

trots Bullseye quickly
Bullseye quickly trots

puns likes Hamm
Hamm likes puns

9

Letter Sounds

Missing Letters

Can you figure out which letter is missing?

r ainbow   **h** elp   l   m

l obster   **m** other   h   r

Read each word out loud.
Listen to the sound of the first letter.

10

I can recognize consonant sounds!

Add the missing letters.

h   i   r   m

Dory **l** oses **h** er dad and mom.
H ow will she find the **r** ight way to go?
L osing them makes **h** er sad.

Read each sentence out loud.
Listen to the letter sounds.
Write your own sentence about Dory.

* Dory loves her mom and dad.

11

Letter Sounds

Who Will Win the Next Race?

Can you figure out which letter is missing?

n   s   t   w

S eason   **W** ater

t axi   **n** ighttime

Read each word out loud.
Listen to the sound of the first letter.
Draw something that begins with n, s, t, or w.

12

I can recognize consonant sounds!

Add the missing letters.

Natalie Certain **W** ants **t** o predict   n
the **n** ext **W** inner.

Lightning McQueen **W** ants **t** o race.   s
"**T** ime for the race!" **S** ays   t
Natalie Certain.   w

Read each sentence out loud.
Listen to the letter sounds.

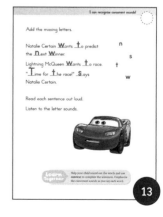

13

---

* Sample answer provided.

192

Page 14

Decode the Secret Messages!

Dash has received a secret message.
Decode the message for him.

Decode this message: k
Party tonight!   P
Go to the garden gate.   d
Bring a kite and a key.   g

Read the message out loud.
Listen to the letter sounds.

14

Page 15

Add the missing letters.

g   p   d   k

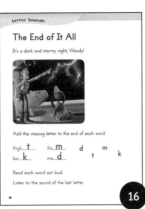

Dash is faster than
a Kangaroo.
Go, Dash, go!!
He leaves the Pack panting behind!
Those kids can't keep up.
People in the crowd
cheer Dash on.

Read each sentence out loud.
Listen to the letter sounds.

15

Page 16

Letter Sounds

The End of It All

It's a dark and stormy night, Woody!

Add the missing letter to the end of each word.

frigh t   fro m   d   t   m   k
loo k   ma d   t   k

Read each word out loud.
Listen to the sound of the last letter.

16

Page 17

Add the missing letter to
the end of each word.

d   t   m   k

Woody will nee d war m clothes
on a col d, dar k nigh t.
Does he wan t to hide under the be d
or rea d a boo k?
Is Woody afrai d of the tric k or treaters?
Le t hi m know everything will be O K.

Read each sentence out loud.
Listen to the letter sounds.

17

Page 18

Letter Sounds

Stop Those Evil Villains!

The Incredibles have a job
to do—stopping the evil villains!
You have a job, too!
Add the missing letter to the end of each word.

p   x   f   l

bo x   ca p
coo l   roo f

Read each word out loud.
Listen to the sound of the last letter.
Use one of the words to write a sentence about
The Incredibles.

* Violet is very cool.

18

Page 19

Add the missing letter to
the end of each word.

Where two letters are
missing in a word, it is
the same two letters.

Can The Incredibles sto p a ll   p
o f the evi l villains?   f
Wi ll they pu ll o ff the   l
rescue? have they the right ma p?   x
They wi ll try to foo l Syndrome and
fi x their jet.

Read each sentence out loud.
Listen to the letter sounds.

19

Page 20

Letter Sounds

Happy Endings

The hermit crabs are mad. Dory needs to flee.

Add the missing letter to the end of each word.

b   s   n   g

crab s   fro g
cra b   dow n

Read each word out loud.
Listen to the sound of the last letter.

20

Page 21

Add the missing letters.

Whe n Dory searche s for her family,   b
every cra b trie s to stop her.   s
Ca n she find them soo n?   n
Dory ha s a bi g problem she need s   g
to solve!

Read each sentence out loud.
Listen to the letter sounds.

21

Page 22

Letter Sounds

Cap or Cape?

The letter a can make a
short vowel sound, as in cap.

It can also make a long vowel sound, as in cape.
Long vowels sound like their names.

Say each word out loud.
Listen for the vowel sound.
Circle the words with a short vowel a sound.

ape (bad) rake (mask) (grab)
grape (Dash) race

Underline the words with a long vowel a sound.

apple raid mad brake cot
shake tame bran

22

Page 23

The letter e can make a
short vowel sound, as in men.
It can also make a long vowel
sound, as in mean.

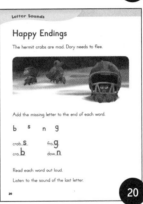

Circle the words with a short
vowel e sound.

(bet) bee (jet) (send) (get)
bead feed (red)

Underline the words with a long vowel e sound.

fed beat met meal meet
set we test

23

Page 24

Letter Sounds

The Fin Is Fine

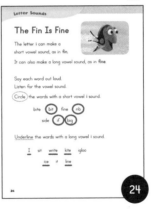

The letter i can make a
short vowel sound, as in fin.

It can also make a long vowel sound, as in fine.

Say each word out loud.
Listen for the vowel sound.
Circle the words with a short vowel i sound.

bite (bit) fine (rib)
side (if) (big)

Underline the words with a long vowel i sound.

I sit write kite igloo
ice it line

24

Page 25

The letter o can make a short
vowel sound, as in not.
It can also make a long vowel
sound, as in note.

Circle the words with a short vowel o sound.

boat (rock) rope (rob) robe
(odd) (top) mole

Underline the words with a long vowel o sound.

open road lock ocean old
soak code pod

25

Page 26

Letter Sounds

Up, Up, and Away!

The letter u can make a short
vowel sound, as in us.
It can also make a long vowel sound, as in use.

Say each word out loud.
Listen for the vowel sound.
Circle the words with a short vowel u sound.

(cut) cute (but) (buggy) (cub)
(truck) (sun) music

Underline the words with a long vowel u sound.

uniform unicorn dull huge
unit bug fuse

26

Page 27

The letter y can sometimes act as a vowel.

What letter sound does the y make in baby? e
What letter sound does the y make in cry?   i

Say each of these words out loud.
Write the vowel sound you hear.
The first one has been done for you.

cry i   sky i   try i
lazy e   oily e   funny e

The letter y can sometimes work with
a vowel to make a long vowel sound.

Say these words out loud: say they tray way

27

Page 28

Letter Sounds

Sarge Battles R

Sometimes, other letters can
make vowels sound different.
For example, in the word Sarge,
a sounds different when followed by r.
The a in Sarge does not sound
long or short.
The r changes the sound of the vowel.
Add the missing vowels.

m a rbles b i rd n u rse f o rk
c a r tig e r b a rn ski i rt
doct o r t u rkey w o rd

Say each word out loud.
Listen to the vowel sound.

28

Page 30

Letter Sounds

Part of the Team

Sometimes, vowels work
together to change a
short vowel sound into
a long vowel sound.

For example, in the word team, the a helps
make the e long.

Say each word out loud. Listen to the
vowel sound.
Underline the two words in each row that make
the same vowel sound.

sleep mean bait
coat green deal
soap feel boat

30

* Sample answer provided.

Answers

The letter e at the end of a word can make the vowel in the middle long.

Sam becomes same when you add a silent e.

The short vowel a sound in Sam becomes a long vowel sound.

Add an e to the end of the end of the purple words below.

Help us us **e** the remote.
Plan to make a plan. **e**
The cop can cop **e**
Take a bit of a bit **e**

Say these sentences out loud.
Listen to the vowel sounds.

31

Freezing Words

Sometimes when two consonants work together in a word you hear both letter sounds.

For example, the F and r in Frozone.

Choose one pair of consonants to make a word.

br tr sl	**br**ick	cl fr bl	**fr**og
fr br sn	**sn**eeze	fl bl cl	**bl**ock
pl st gr	**gr**ain	dr cr st	**st**eam

32

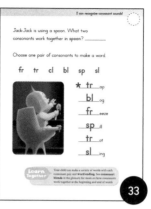

Jack-Jack is using a spoon. What two consonants work together in spoon? _____

Choose one pair of consonants to make a word.

fr   tr   cl   bl   sp   sl

* trap
blog
freeze
spill
trot
sling

33

Sticking Together to the End

Two or more consonants can also work together at the end of a word.

Hank is Dory's friend.

Listen to the sounds the letters nd make.

Choose one pair of consonants to make a word.

lp nt lt	he**lp**	nt nd mp	ba**nd**	st lp rd	bi**rd**
st pt ct	te**st**	pt nt mp	la**mp**	lf nt rd	elepha**nt**

34

Choose one pair of consonants to make a word.

rd   st   nt   nd   mp

Becky is a bi**rd** called a loon.

Dory mu**st** ju**mp** into a drain to escape.

Dory looks differe**nt** from the other fish in the ocean.

Where will Dory's story e**nd**?

Read the sentences out loud.

35

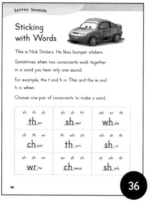

Sticking with Words

This is Nick Stickers. He likes bumper stickers.

Sometimes when two consonants work together in a word you hear only one sound.

For example, the t and h in This and the w and h in when.

Choose one pair of consonants to make a word.

sh th ch	**th**an	sh ch th	**sh**eet	wh wr th	**wh**ale
ch th wr	**ch**eat	ch th sh	**th**orn	wh sh th	**sh**ut
sh ch wr	**wr**ite	wr sh ch	**ch**eese	sh wh th	**sh**ark

36

Read these bumper stickers out loud.

Underline the consonants that work together to make one sound.

CHOOSE THE CHASE!

Through Thick or Thin, We Play to Win!

shape up ship out

I stayed in sleepy Radiator Springs

Where Wishes Come True!

Big Dreams in the Trunk

37

Shhhh!

Buzz has hit the mute button!

Some words have letters that you don't pronounce.

These letters are called silent letters.

The letters b, g, h, k, and w are sometimes silent.

Underline the silent letters in Buzz Lightyear's name.

Say each of these words out loud.
Underline the silent letters.

thumb   sign   knock   wrist   light

comb   write   ghost   knife   right

38

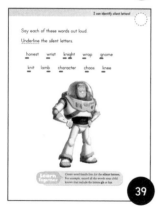

Say each of these words out loud.
Underline the silent letters.

honest   wrist   knight   wrap   gnome

knit   lamb   character   chaos   knee

39

Inside Outside Words

You never know what's hiding inside!

A compound word is made using two smaller words.

Draw a / between the two smaller words in the word inside.

Draw a / between the two smaller words inside each word below.

The first one has been done for you.

can/hot   anybody   campfire   today

anyone   everything   basketball   without

cupcake   sunshine   rainfall   forever

40

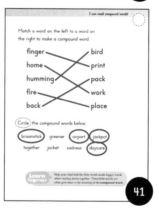

Match a word on the left to a word on the right to make a compound word.

finger ——— bird
home —— print
humming —— pack
fire —— work
back ——— place

Circle the compound words below.

(broomstick)   greener   (airport)   (jackpot)
together   jacket   sadness   (daycare)

41

Don't Forget, We're Superheroes

A contraction is a word that is made by joining two words.

An apostrophe takes the place of any missing letters.

Match each contraction below with the two words that have been joined.

don't ——— I am
we're —— you are
you're —— he is
I'm —— do not
he's ——— we are

42

Fill in the missing contraction to complete each sentence.

You're about to read an amazing story.

The Incredibles **haven't** had any luck lately.

They **can't** fly their jet.

It's broken.

And that evil villain, Syndrome, is after them. **He's** out to get them.

He's
can't
haven't
It's
You're

Use one of the contractions to write a sentence about superheroes.

* It's hard being a superhero.

43

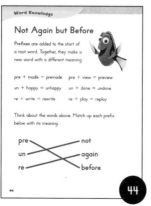

Not Again but Before

Prefixes are added to the start of a root word. Together, they make a new word with a different meaning.

pre + made = premade   pre + view = preview
un + happy = unhappy   un + done = undone
re + write = rewrite   re + play = replay

Think about the words above. Match up each prefix below with its meaning.

pre ——— not
un —— again
re —— before

44

Fill in the missing prefix to complete each sentence below.

You may use each prefix more than once.

Dory is **un**happy when she can't find her parents.

She **re**visits every place they have been together.

Dory is having trouble finding her parents, **un**fortunately.

Will her parents ever **re**appear?

un
re

Add a prefix to a word to make a new word.

* un + **do** = **undo**

45

More and Most

Suffixes are added to the end of a word to make a new word.

For example, Lightning McQueen is big, but Taco is bigger. Miss Fritter is the biggest.

Add the root word to its suffix.

Print the new word.

kind + er = **kinder**
kind + est = **kindest**
kind + ness = **kindness**
long + er = **longer**
long + est = **longest**

46

* Sample answer provided.

I can use suffixes to make words!

Try adding -er, -est, and -ness to each of the following words.

sweet sweeter sweetest sweetness
soft softer softest softness
hard harder hardest hardness

Think about what each word means.
Label each wheel using small, smaller, smallest.

small smaller smallest

I can identify homophones!

Use the correct homophone in each sentence.

We a t e our lunch together. ate eight

I wonder w h e r e Woody has gone. wear where

Bo Peep sees them going over t h e r e ? there their

What do you want t o do today? too two to

Why do you w e a r that cowboy hat, Woody? where wear

I can identify nouns!

Underline the nouns in each sentence.

Mr. Incredible has strong arms that can lift boulders.

Can Dash run faster than a rocket heading to the moon?

Elastigirl can stretch her whole body around a car.

The villain reveals his evil plan as he rises into the sky.

Word Knowledge

Action!

A verb is an action word.
A verb often follows a noun.
The verb is the "doing" word.

Underline the verbs below.

swim purple play talk look Dory
food sing ocean laugh eat learn

Pick an action word.
Draw a picture of Dory doing that action.

I can identify verbs!

When you add a verb to a sentence, how the verb is spelled depends on the noun it appears with. We swim fast, but she swims faster.
Underline the verbs below. Think about how the verb is spelled.

Dory sees lots of other fish in the ocean.
I see Dory.

Dory looks for her parents.
Her parents look for her, too.

Dory has a yellow tail. I have no tail.

Dory plays with her friends in the ocean.
I play with my friends at school.

Word Knowledge

Action Now and Then!

When you add a verb to a sentence, how the verb is spelled depends on when the action takes place.

Andy **played** yesterday. Andy **plays** again today.
past present

The word **played** is the past tense of **play**.
Underline the verbs below that are in the past tense.

looked walked see
treated dream wished

I can identify verb tense!

Underline the verbs in the sentences below.
Think about how the verbs are spelled.

Yesterday: The children dressed. They ate breakfast. They got on the bus. They went to school.

Today: The children dress. They eat breakfast. They get on the bus. They go to school.

Write another sentence for yesterday.
* Yesterday, I played outside.

Write another sentence for today.
* Today, I have a karate lesson.

Word Knowledge

Describe It!

An adjective is a word that describes a noun.
Riley is **happy**. The word **happy** describes Riley.

Add one of these adjectives to a sentence below.

big little blue

Riley is a l i t t l e girl.
Riley's eyes are b l u e.
Riley has a b i g problem.

Write a sentence to describe yourself.
Use an adjective.
* I have curly hair.

* Sample answer provided.

Answers

I can use descriptive words!

An adverb is a word that describes a verb.

It tells when, where, how, or what.

These are adverbs:

now, loudly, under, inside, carefully

Riley jumps around **happily**.

The word **happily** describes how Riley is jumping.

Add each of these adverbs to a sentence below.

softly   slowly   later   outside

Riley goes **o u t s i d e** to play.

Riley walks **s l o w l y**.

She whispers **s o f t l y**.

Riley will be happy again **l a t e r**.

57

Comprehension

Evil Robot Attacks City!

Clues in the text and picture can help you make predictions.

Look at the picture. Predict what the story on page 59 is about. ***The Incredibles are all trying to stop an evil robot.***

58

I can make predictions!

An evil robot is attacking the city.

The Incredibles must stop it.

Mr. Incredible knows the robot is controlled by the remote.

Frozone uses ice walls to slow down the robot.

Elastigirl aims the remote at the robot.

* I'm sure that **The Incredibles will win the battle because The Incredibles are superheroes!**

59

I can make connections!

Dory forgets where her parents are.

She wants to be with them again.

Hank wants to help. He rescues Dory from the tank.

Hank helps Dory find a map.

A purple shell on the map is a clue.

Dory knows where to look next.

Underline the words in the story that remind you of something.

Explain any connections you made.

* **I got lost in the mall. I was scared and needed help.**

61

I can identify story elements!

1 One day, a man steals Woody and takes him to his apartment.

2 Woody tries to escape. That's when he meets Jessie and Bullseye.

3 Jessie tells Woody that he is the star of a show called "Woody's Roundup."

4 Woody needs to decide: stay with his new friends or return to Andy and his old friends.

Circle the characters in this story.

Underline the setting.

Number the events in the story.

63

I can identify main idea!

One day, Dory is carried away from her parents by an undertow.

Dory loses her parents for a long time.

Dory has trouble remembering things.

Dory forgets where to find her parents.

She meets her friends Nemo and Marlin.

For a while she lives with them in a coral reef.

Finally, she remembers her parents.

What is the main idea in this story?

* **The main idea is that Dory is trying to find her parents.**

65

I can make pictures in my mind!

Woody and Buzz race down the street on the remote-control car.

Woody is crouched in front, leaning over the car's bumper. His face is full of fear.

A rocket is strapped to Buzz's back. Buzz sits behind Woody, holding the remote control. Buzz has a look of concentration on his face as he works the remote.

Underline the words that help you form a picture of the scene in your mind.

* Describe what you see. **I picture Woody and Buzz zooming down the street.**

67

I can make inferences!

Bob, Helen, Violet, Dash, and Jack-Jack Parr live in Metroville. They all have superpowers.

Unfortunately, they are not allowed to use them in public. The Parr family pretends they are like other people. Bob is bored. Dash pretends to be a slower runner.

The whole family is worried they will never again have the chance to be superheroes. Until one day, a villain is spotted over Metroville.

How do you think the Parrs feel about not using their superpowers?

* **The Parrs miss being able to use their superpowers.**

69

I can draw conclusions!

Riley and her family move from Minnesota to San Francisco. Riley is so sad she runs away.

Joy wants Riley to be happy. She does not want Sadness to take control because Riley will be sad.

Finally, Joy learns that she and Sadness must work together to help Riley. Joy decides that Riley needs to feel sad sometimes in order to feel happy.

Do you agree with Joy's decision? Why?

* **Yes. It's ok to feel sad if you move.**

71

I can identify facts and opinions!

This is a fact: Most cars have four wheels.

This is an opinion: I think all cars should be yellow.

Write F beside each fact and O beside each opinion.

O I think trucks are better than cars.

F Trucks are bigger than cars.

F Trucks can hold more stuff than cars.

O The nicest looking trucks are blue ones with big tires.

O Trucks are more fun to ride in than cars.

F Most trucks have windows.

73

---

* Sample answer provided.

Extra Information

Labels give you extra information.

They help you understand pictures better.

Fill in the missing labels.

blue hair   **face**

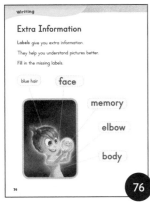

memory

elbow

body

76

Captions are sentences that tell you what is happening in a picture.

They can give you more information about the picture.

Write a caption for each picture.

* **Joy looks at one of Riley's memories.**   **Joy and Sadness meet Bing Bong.**

77

Create a chart with the information on page 78. The first column has been filled for you.

Number of Practice Races Won

Lightning McQueen	Cruz Ramirez	Cal Weathers	Brick Yardley
8	3	7	2

Who has won the most practice races?

Lightning McQueen

Who has won the fewest practice races?

Brick Yardley

How many more practice races has Lightning McQueen won than Cal Weathers?   **1**

79

Write three facts about Woody, Bullseye, or Jessie.

* 1 **Woody dresses like a cowboy.**

* 2 **Woody is a sheriff.**

* 3 **Woody rides a horse named Bullseye.**

83

Writing Sentences

Sentences end in different types of **punctuation**.

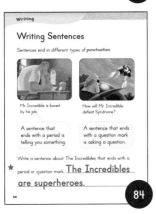

Mr. Incredible is bored by his job.

How will Mr. Incredible defeat Syndrome?

A sentence that ends with a period is telling you something.

A sentence that ends with a question mark is asking a question.

Write a sentence about The Incredibles that ends with a period or question mark. **The Incredibles are superheroes.**

84

The Incredibles are trapped!

Save the family, Violet!

A sentence that ends with an exclamation mark can show excitement or surprise.

An exclamation mark at the end of a sentence can also be a command.

Write a sentence about The Incredibles that ends with an exclamation mark. **The Incredibles save the day!**

85

Add the missing commas to the sentences below.

I like to eat cereal, apples, and toast.

After eating, I brush my teeth.

If you ride a bike, you should wear a helmet.

My favourite colours are orange, red, and purple.

87

Belonging and More

An **apostrophe** can be used to show that something belongs to someone. This is an apostrophe: '

Nemo is Marlin's son.

Dory's friends are Marlin, Nemo, Hank, Destiny, and Bailey.

Add an apostrophe to each sentence.

Dory's parents set out shell trails.

Hank's arms are really long.

88

A **contraction** is two words put together. The missing letters are replaced by an apostrophe.

For example, is not becomes isn't.

Make contractions with the words below, adding an apostrophe.

I have **I've**   we will **we'll**

we are **we're**   they have **they've**

let us **let's**   you are **you're**

he is **he's**   she is **she's**

should not **shouldn't**   would not **wouldn't**

89

Say It

Quotation marks show that someone is speaking. These are quotation marks: " "

These marks are often used with the words **said** or **asked**.

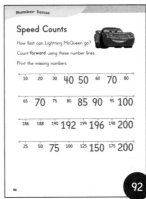

"Hello, Mr. Incredible," says a woman on the screen.

"Why can't we come, Mom?" Violet asks.

Look at the picture on the right. Write what Mom's reply might be. Use quotation marks.

* **"It's too dangerous!" says Mom.**

90

Speed Counts

How fast can Lightning McQueen go?

Count **forward** using these number lines.

Print the missing numbers.

10 20 30 **40** **50** 60 **70** 80

65 **70** 75 80 **85** **90** 95 **100**

186 188 190 **192** 194 **196** 198 **200**

25 50 **75** 100 **125** **150** 175 **200**

92

Print the missing numbers on the 100-chart.

100	101	102	103	104	105	106	107	108	109
110	111	112	113	114	115	116	117	118	119
120	121	122	123	124	125	126	127	128	129
130	131	132	133	134	135	136	137	138	139
140	141	142	143	144	145	146	147	148	149
150	151	152	153	154	155	156	157	158	159
160	161	162	163	164	165	166	167	168	169
170	171	172	173	174	175	176	177	178	179
180	181	182	183	184	185	186	187	188	189
190	191	192	193	194	195	196	197	198	199

93

Countdown!

How many days will it take for Dory to find her parents?

Count **backward** using these number lines.

Print the missing numbers.

50 **49** 48 **47** 46 **45** 44 **43**

47 46 45 **44** **43** **42** 41 **40**

90 **80** 70 60 **50** 40 **30** 20 10

100 **90** 80 **70** **60** 50 40 **30**

94

Print the missing numbers on the 100-chart.

100	99	98	97	96	95	94	93	92	91
90	89	88	87	86	85	84	83	82	81
80	79	78	77	76	75	74	73	72	71
70	69	68	67	66	65	64	63	62	61
60	59	58	57	56	55	54	53	52	51
50	49	48	47	46	45	44	43	42	41
40	39	38	37	36	35	34	33	32	31
30	29	28	27	26	25	24	23	22	21
20	19	18	17	16	15	14	13	12	11
10	9	8	7	6	5	4	3	2	1

95

Super Frames

How many blobs of goo are flying at Mr. Incredible?

Draw 23 squishy blobs of goo.

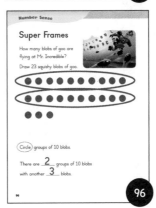

Circle groups of 10 blobs.

There are **2** groups of 10 blobs with another **3** blobs.

96

---

* Sample answer provided.

Answers

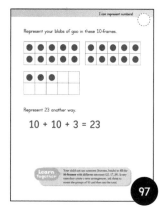

I can represent numbers!

Represent your blobs of goo in these 10-frames.

Represent 23 another way.

$10 + 10 + 3 = 23$

Learn Together Your child can use counters (buttons, beads) to fill the 10-frames with different amounts (23, 17, 29). Every time they create a new arrangement, ask them to count the groups of 10 and then say the total.

97

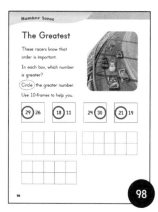

Number Sense

The Greatest

These racers know that order is important.

In each box, which number is greater?

(Circle) the greater number.

Use 10-frames to help you.

(29) 26   (18) 11   24 (30)   (21) 19

98

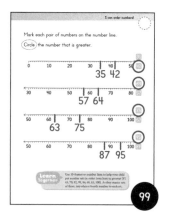

I can order numbers!

Mark each pair of numbers on the number line.

(Circle) the number that is greater.

35 (42)

57 (64)

(63) 75

(87) 95

Learn Together Use 10-frames or number lines to help your child put number sets in order: from least to greatest (63, 65, 70, 82, 95, 84, 68, 81, 100). As they master sets of three, introduce a fourth number to each set.

99

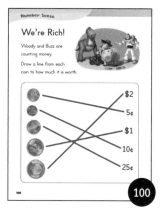

Number Sense

We're Rich!

Woody and Buzz are counting money.

Draw a line from each coin to how much it is worth.

$2
5¢
$1
10¢
25¢

100

I can count money!

Show 25¢ in 2 ways.

* | 1 quarter | 2 dimes and 1 nickel |

Show 50¢ in 2 ways.

* | 2 quarters | 5 dimes |

Show $1 in 2 ways.

* | 4 quarters | 10 dimes |

Learn Together Work with your child to figure out other ways to show these amounts. Use coins to help them.

101

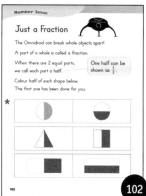

Number Sense

Just a Fraction

The Omnidroid can break whole objects apart!

A part of a whole is called a fraction.

When there are 2 equal parts, we call each part a half.

One half can be shown as $\frac{1}{2}$.

Colour half of each shape below.

The first one has been done for you.

*

102

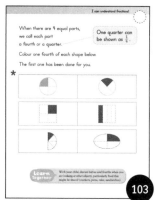

I can understand fractions!

When there are 4 equal parts, we call each part a fourth or a quarter.

One quarter can be shown as $\frac{1}{4}$.

Colour one fourth of each shape below.

The first one has been done for you.

Learn Together With your child, discuss halves and fourths when you are looking at other objects, particularly food that might be shared (crackers, pizza, cake, sandwiches).

103

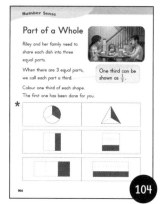

Number Sense

Part of a Whole

Riley and her family need to share each dish into three equal parts.

When there are 3 equal parts, we call each part a third.

One third can be shown as $\frac{1}{3}$.

Colour one third of each shape.

The first one has been done for you.

*

104

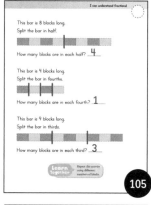

I can understand fractions!

This bar is 8 blocks long.
Split the bar in half.

How many blocks are in each half? __4__

This bar is 4 blocks long.
Split the bar in fourths.

How many blocks are in each fourth? __1__

This bar is 9 blocks long.
Split the bar in thirds.

How many blocks are in each third? __3__

Learn Together Repeat this activity using different numbers of blocks.

105

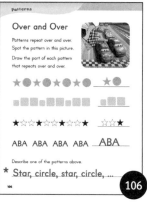

Patterns

Over and Over

Patterns repeat over and over. Spot the pattern in this picture. Draw the part of each pattern that repeats over and over.

★●★●★●★● ● ___★●___

___■●___

★☆☆★☆☆★☆☆★ ___☆☆★___

ABA ABA ABA ABA ___ABA___

Describe one of the patterns above.

* Star, circle, star, circle, ...

106

* Sample answer provided.

Page 107

Patterns can change by size, shape, colour, or direction.

Draw the part of each pattern that repeats.

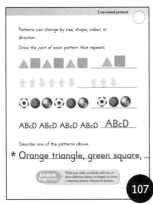

ABcD ABcD ABcD ABcD __ABcD__

Describe one of the patterns above.

* Orange triangle, green square, ...

107

Page 108

Colourful Patterns

What patterns do you see in this picture?

Finish each of the patterns below by adding colour.

108

Page 110

Growing and Shrinking

Extend each pattern.

Circle if the pattern is shrinking or growing.

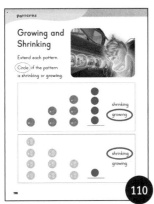

shrinking / (growing)

shrinking / growing

110

Page 111

Extend each pattern.

Circle if the pattern is shrinking or growing.

5 10 15 20 25 30 __35__   shrinking / (growing)

EEEEE EEEE EEE __EE__   (shrinking) / growing

32 30 28 26 24 22 __20__   (shrinking) / growing

111

Page 112

Skipping Along

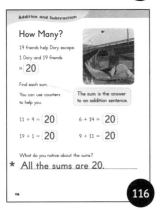

__5__ __10__ __15__ __20__

Each bookshelf can hold 5 books.

Skip count by 5s.

How many books are there in total? __20__

Hamm holds 4 quarters.

Skip count by 25s.

__25¢__ __50¢__ __75¢__ __$1__

How much money is there in total? __$1__

112

Page 113

Use a number line to help you skip count.

This number line shows skip counting by 5s.

0 1 2 3 4 5 6 7 8 9 10 11 12 13 14 15 16 17 18 19 20

Find the next 3 numbers.

5, 7, __9__, __11__, __13__

10, 12, __14__, __16__, __18__

3, 6, __9__, __12__, __15__

4, 8, __12__, __16__, __20__

113

Page 114

It All Adds Up

How many times do Fluke and Rudder bark at Gerald?

3 + 6 = __9__   9 + 9 = __18__

4 + 2 = __6__   11 + 5 = __16__

7 + 10 = __17__   4 + 8 = __12__

14 + 2 = __16__

114

Page 115

Look at the 10-frames.

Write the addition sentences.

__10__ + __4__ = __14__

__7__ + __10__ = __17__

__10__ + __9__ = __19__

115

Page 116

How Many?

19 friends help Dory escape.

1 Dory and 19 friends is __20__

Find each sum.

You can use counters to help you.

The sum is the answer to an addition sentence.

11 + 9 = __20__   6 + 14 = __20__

19 + 1 = __20__   9 + 11 = __20__

What do you notice about the sums?

* All the sums are 20.

116

Page 117

Find each sum.

You can use counters to help you.

12 + 8 = __20__   15 + 5 = __20__

3 + 17 = __20__   5 + 15 = __20__

What do you notice about the sums?

* All the sums are 20.

Write another addition sentence that fits with the ones above.

* 14 + 6 = 20

117

Page 118

Adding Nothing

Read this addition story.

7 friends are playing a game.

No other friends want to play.

How many friends are playing the game?

This addition story can be written as an addition sentence.

7 + 0 = 7

Find each sum.

20 + 0 = __20__   0 + 11 = __11__

12 + 0 = __12__   17 + 0 = __17__

What do you notice when you add 0 to a number?

* The number doesn't change.

118

Page 119

How many friends are playing in this picture?

No one joins them.

Write the addition sentence for this story.

__12__ + __0__ = __12__

Find each sum.

18 + 0 = __18__   0 + 25 = __25__

31 + 0 = __31__   0 + 14 = __14__

49 + 0 = __49__   50 + 0 = __50__

119

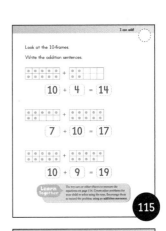

* Sample answer provided.

Answers

You can also solve 10 + 14 by making friendly numbers.

10 + 14

10 + 10 + 4 = 24

So, 10 + 14 = 24

Find each sum.

13 + 10 = **23**   15 + 10 = **25**

16 + 10 = **26**   17 + 10 = **27**

20 + 10 = **30**   20 + 13 = **33**

20 + 15 = **35**   20 + 20 = **40**

20 + 21 = **41**   20 + 22 = **42**

121

Addition and Subtraction

Add That Cash

Money is kept in cash registers.

Look at the coins.

Write addition sentences.

Figure out how much money is in total.

5¢ + 10¢ = **15¢**

25¢ + 10¢ = **35¢**

122

Look at the coins.

Estimate, then find the total.

+   = | **35¢**
Estimate | Total

+   = | **45¢**
Estimate | Total

+   = | **70¢**
Estimate | Total

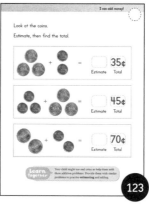

123

Addition and Subtraction

I "Otter" Take Some Away

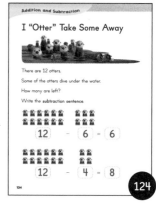

There are 12 otters.

Some of the otters dive under the water.

How many are left?

Write the subtraction sentence.

12 − **6** = **6**

12 − **4** = **8**

124

Look at the 10-frames.

Write the subtraction sentences.

10 − **4** = **6**

10 − **6** = **4**

10 − **9** = **1**

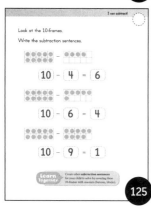

125

Addition and Subtraction

What's Left?

There are 4 toys all together.

Then 1 toy falls.

How many are left?

4 − 1 = **3**

Subtract to find each difference.

The difference is the answer to a subtraction sentence.

9 − 1 = **8**   7 − 3 = **4**

14 − 1 = **13**   8 − 3 = **5**

18 − 4 = **14**   12 − 4 = **8**

17 − 4 = **13**   16 − 4 = **12**

126

There are 5 toys all together.

1 toy leaves.

How many are left?

5 − 1 = **4**

Subtract to find each difference.

18 − 2 = **16**   20 − 2 = **18**

18 − 3 = **15**   20 − 3 = **17**

18 − 4 = **14**   24 − 4 = **20**

18 − 5 = **13**   25 − 5 = **20**

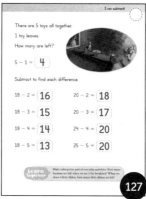

127

Addition and Subtraction

Take Away Nothing!

Read this subtraction story.

Riley has 5 emotions. Riley needs all her emotions.

None of the emotions should be blocked.

− 0 =

Solve these subtraction sentences.

18 − 0 = **18**   10 − 0 = **10**

11 − 0 = **11**   17 − 0 = **17**

What do you notice when you subtract 0 from a number?

The number doesn't change

128

Solve these subtraction sentences.

Use counters or 10-frames to help you.

17 − 1 = **16**   16 − 5 = **11**

13 − 3 = **10**   12 − 3 = **9**

15 − 4 = **11**   19 − 6 = **13**

18 − 0 = **18**   11 − 1 = **10**

20 − 5 = **15**   14 − 4 = **10**

16 − 3 = **13**   18 − 5 = **13**

12 − 4 = **8**   15 − 0 = **15**

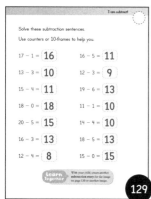

129

Find each difference.

22 − 10 = **12**   23 − 10 = **13**

24 − 10 = **14**   26 − 10 = **16**

29 − 10 = **19**   38 − 20 = **18**

40 − 10 = **30**   43 − 10 = **33**

45 − 10 = **35**   50 − 10 = **40**

33 − 20 = **13**   38 − 20 = **18**

40 − 30 = **10**   44 − 30 = **14**

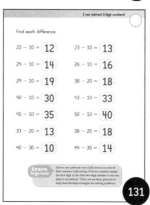

131

Addition and Subtraction

Less Cash

Look at the coins.

Figure out how much money is

10¢ − 5¢ = **5¢**

25¢ − 10¢ = **15¢**

$1 − 25¢ = **75¢**

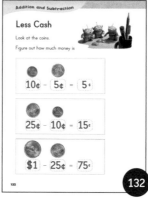

132

Look at the coins.

Figure out how much money is left.

−   = **20¢**

= **15¢**

= **40¢**

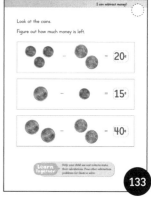

133

Addition and Subtraction

Adding Up and Taking Away

The otters are happy to have Dory for a friend!

If you know that

4 otters + 1 Dory = 5 friends,

then you know that 5 − 1 = 4.

Use the addition sentences to solve the related subtraction sentences.

8 + 5 = 13   13 − 5 = **8**

5 + 6 = 11   11 − 5 = **6**

9 + 8 = 17   17 − 8 = **9**

7 + 9 = 16   16 − 9 = **7**

134

Use the subtraction sentences to help you solve the related addition sentences.

14 − 8 = 6   8 + 6 = **14**

16 − 6 = 10   6 + 10 = **16**

18 − 7 = 11   7 + 11 = **18**

17 − 8 = 9   8 + 9 = **17**

15 − 5 = 10   5 + 10 = **15**

13 − 8 = 5   8 + 5 = **13**

11 − 6 = 5   6 + 5 = **11**

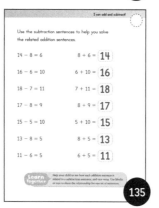

135

Addition and Subtraction

Quick Calculations

Can you be as fast as Dash?

What can you add or subtract to change the first number into the final number?

The first one is done for you.

20 − 2 = 18   7 **+11** = 18

8 **+11** = 19   17 **−6** = 11

12 **−9** = 3   20 **+5** = 25

5 **+10** = 15   16 **−12** = 4

136

---

7 **−2** = 5   24 **−12** = 12

11 **+4** = 15   13 **+8** = 21

9 **+8** = 17   22 **+3** = 25

16 **−4** = 12   15 **−6** = 9

25 **−5** = 20   14 **+7** = 21

8 **−4** = 4   6 **+6** = 12

20 **−10** = 10   10 **+10** = 20

137

---

* Sample answer provided.

Page 138

Joining Equal Groups

You multiply when you join equal groups.

Here are 4 groups of 2 fish.

There are 8 fish altogether.

$4 \times 2 = 8$

> This is another way to show the word multiply.

Here are 3 groups of 3 fish.

There are 9 fish altogether.

138

Page 139

Here are 3 groups of 4 fish.

There are 12 fish altogether.

$3 \times 4 = 12$

Here are 4 groups of 3 fish.

There are 12 fish altogether.

$4 \times 3 = 12$

139

Page 140

Let's Multiply

Flo has many barrels of oil. You can multiply to find out how many she has.

There are 3 groups of 2 barrels.
There are 6 barrels all together.
$3 \times 2 = 6$

There are 2 groups of 3 barrels.

$2 \times 3 = 6$

140

Page 141

There are 6 groups of 2 barrels.

$6 \times 2 = 12$

There are 7 groups of 2 barrels.

$7 \times 2 = 14$

There are 3 groups of 3 barrels.

$3 \times 3 = 9$

141

Page 142

Counting Groups

Edna Mode buys lots of masks for the Supers.

How many masks are there?

Circle every group of 2 masks.

Fill in the boxes.

$2 + 2 + 2 + 2 + 2 + 2 = 12$

There are 6 groups of 2.

$6 \times 2 = 12$

There are 12 masks.

142

Page 143

More masks just arrived! How many masks are there?

Circle every group of 3 masks.

Fill in the boxes.

$3 + 3 + 3 + 3 = 12$

There are 4 groups of 3.

$4 \times 3 = 12$

There are 12 masks.

143

Page 144

Separating Equal Groups

You divide when you want to share a group in equal parts.

1 race car has 4 tires.

How many race cars share 8 tires?

2 race cars.

How many race cars share 12 tires?

3 race cars.

144

Page 145

How many race cars share 16 tires?

4 race cars.

How many race cars share 20 tires?

5 race cars.

How many race cars share 24 tires?

6 race cars.

145

* Sample answer provided.

Answers

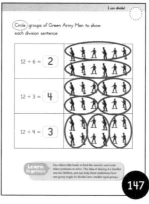

147

Circle groups of Green Army Men to show each division sentence

12 ÷ 6 = **2**	
12 ÷ 3 = **4**	
12 ÷ 4 = **3**	

Learn together Use objects like beads to find the answer and create other problems to solve. The idea of sharing is a familiar one for children, and can help them understand how one group might be divided into smaller equal groups.

148

Multiplication and Division

Making Equal Groups

Show how the 10 fish below can be divided equally into 2 parts of the reef.

Each part of the reef has **5** fish.

I can divide!

149

You have 20 marbles.

Fill each box with an equal number of marbles to show each division sentence.

20 ÷ 4 = **5**

20 ÷ 5 = **4**

20 ÷ 10 = **2**

Learn together Help your child figure out how to fill the boxes. Ask, "Is there another way to share the marbles equally?" (2 boxes with 10 marbles each; 20 boxes with 1 marble each).

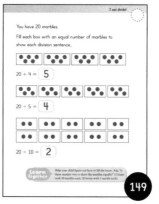

153

I can measure!

Circle the unit of measurement that is most appropriate to measure the giraffe and the girl.

cm
(m)
(cm)
m

How tall are you?

I am about ____ cm tall.

I am about ____ m tall.

Learn together Help your child measure their height. Measure other objects using centimetres and metres.

Measurement

Hold It!

Fillmore wants to know which containers hold about the same.

Circle the objects in each row that hold about the same.

154

I can compare volume!

Estimate how many glasses of water each container will hold.

Circle the container that holds the most.

Container	Estimate	Actual Measurement
pitcher		
pot		
pan		

Learn together Provide your child with a glass and the other containers to help them estimate, and then measure how much each will hold. Find other containers around your home and create a chart like the one above.

155

Measurement

Heavy or Light?

It's the Incredible family! Who do you think is the heaviest?

Mr. Incredible

Circle the object in each pair that is heavier.

156

I can compare mass!

You can use a pan balance to compare the mass of two objects.

If you put two objects on a pan balance, how do you know which one is lighter?

***** **The lighter object will be on the side of the scale that is higher than the other side.**

Learn together Help your child compare the mass of objects using a pan balance, or a kitchen or bathroom scale. Note that your child may not yet have been introduced to units of measurement for mass.

157

Measurement

How Big?

Estimate the number of squares that cover this picture. ☐

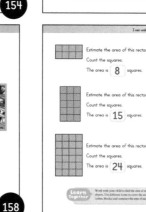

Now count the number of squares that cover the picture. **24**

You figured out the area of the picture.

Area is the amount of space inside of a shape.

158

I can understand area!

Estimate the area of this rectangle. ☐
Count the squares.
The area is **8** squares.

Estimate the area of this rectangle. ☐
Count the squares.
The area is **15** squares.

Estimate the area of this rectangle. ☐
Count the squares.
The area is **24** squares.

Learn together Work with your child to find the area of other objects. Use different items to cover the surface (cubes, blocks) and compare the size of each surface.

159

Measurement

Counting the Days

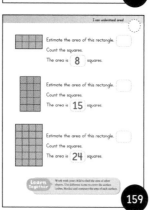

Woody is interested in the calendar on Andy's wall.

Arrange these in order from shortest to longest.

month   week   year   day

day   week   month   year

How many months are in 1 year? **12**

How many days are in 1 week? **7**

Some months have 31 days.
Some months have 30 days.
February has 28 days, except every 4 years it has 29.

160

Measurement

Time Enough

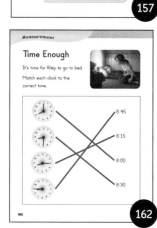

It's time for Riley to go to bed. Match each clock to the correct time.

8:45
8:15
8:00
8:30

162

***** Sample answer provided.

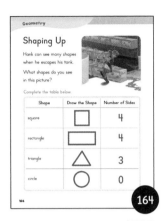

Shaping Up

Hank can see many shapes when he escapes his tank. What shapes do you see in this picture?

Complete the table below.

Shape	Draw the Shape	Number of Sides
square	□	4
rectangle	▭	4
triangle	△	3
circle	○	0

164

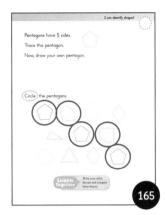

I can identify shapes!

Pentagons have 5 sides.
Trace this pentagon.
Now, draw your own pentagon.

Circle the pentagons.

165

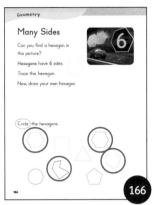

Many Sides

Can you find a hexagon in this picture? Hexagons have 6 sides. Trace this hexagon. Now, draw your own hexagon.

Circle the hexagons.

166

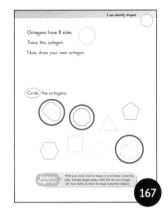

I can identify shapes!

Octagons have 8 sides.
Trace this octagon.
Now, draw your own octagon.

Circle the octagons.

167

All Sorts of Shapes

Woody is trapped in a crate. The crate is made up of a lot of quadrilaterals. Quadrilaterals have 4 sides.

Squares, rectangles, diamonds, and rhombuses are all quadrilaterals.

Circle the quadrilaterals.

168

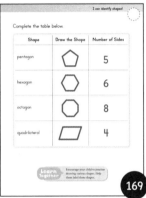

I can identify shapes!

Complete the table below.

Shape	Draw the Shape	Number of Sides
pentagon	⬠	5
hexagon	⬡	6
octagon	⯃	8
quadrilateral	▱	4

169

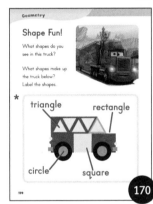

Shape Fun!

What shapes do you see in this truck?

What shapes make up the truck below? Label the shapes.

* triangle rectangle circle square

170

Power Objects

Circle the 3-D objects you see in this picture.

Use these words to name each 3-D object below.

cube   cone   cylinder   sphere

cylinder   cube

sphere   cone

Name one of the 3-D objects you circled in the picture.

* cylinder

172

* Sample answer provided.

Use the clues to answer these riddles.

All my faces are the same and I have 8 vertices.

What am I? __cube__

I have one vertex and can roll.

What am I? __cone__

edge

vertex

face

I have flat faces and can be stacked.

What am I? __cylinder__

I have no vertices and can roll.

What am I? __sphere__

Learn Together Help your child create other riddles for 3-D objects. Your child can create 3-D objects using modelling clay or other materials. They can describe and label the objects.

173

Geometry

In 3-D

What 3-D objects do you see in this picture?

Pyramids and prisms are also 3-D objects.

Use these words to name each 3-D object below.

triangular prism   cone pyramid
rectangular prism

__cone pyramid__

__triangular prism__

__rectangular prism__

174

Use the clues to answer these riddles.

edge   vertex

face

I have six faces and can stack.

What am I? __rectangular prism__

I have five faces and five vertices.

What am I? __cone pyramid__

I have two triangular faces and three rectangular faces.

What am I? __triangular prism__

Write another riddle for one 3-D object.

Learn Together Talk about how write shapes can roll and some shapes can stack. Lund some can do both. Use blocks or other objects to experiment to find out which 3-D objects are best for stacking and rolling.

175

Start at Erica's house.

Walk east along Queen Street.

Turn north on Oak Road. Walk to the end of the street.

Where are you? __hospital__

Write directions from the hospital to the store.

* Walk south on Oak St.
Turn west on Main St.
Walk past Ash Rd.

Write directions from the community centre to the library.

* Walk west on Main St.
Walk past Ash Rd.

Learn Together Examine the map together. Help your child create a map of your neighbourhood. As you work, use phrases such as behind, next, far, and in front of to describe location. Use the map or create directions for another person to follow.

177

Collecting and Using Data

What Are the Chances?

Jackson Storm	Chuck Armstrong
Lightning McQueen	Manny Flywheel
	Cruz Ramirez

Look at the picture.

Circle the word that best describes each statement.

Lightning McQueen will win the race.

likely   unlikely   certain   impossible

Chuck Armstrong will win the race.

likely   unlikely   certain   **impossible**

175

178

Manny Flywheel will win the race.

likely   **unlikely**   certain   impossible

Chuck Armstrong will finish the race before Jackson Storm.

likely   **unlikely**   certain   impossible

This race will have a winner.

likely   unlikely   **certain**   impossible

Write your own probability statement about the race.

* Lightning McQueen will come
in last place. (Unlikley)

Learn Together Discuss the meaning of each **probability** phrase with your child. Encourage them to use one of these phrases as they write a new statement. Play games with spinners or dice to help your child learn about probability.

179

Collecting and Using Data

Picturing Numbers

A bar graph uses bars to show data.

How Riley Feels

Riley feels Joy __5__ times.

She feels Sadness __1__ time.

She feels Anger __3__ times.

180

180

Collecting and Using Data

Graph Up

Woody asks his friends what colour he should paint the house.

Their paint colour choices are on this line plot.

A line plot uses an x to show how many times something happened.

House Paint Colours

How many friends want the house to be blue? __5__

182

182

* Sample answer provided.

Congratulations

to

_____

for completing this workbook!
Keep up the good work!